AQA A2 Biology:

Writing the Synoptic Essay

by

Dr Robert Mitchell

CT Publications

A catalogue record for this book is available from the British Library

ISBN 978-1-907769-00-9

First published in May 2010 by
CT Publications

Copyright © Dr Robert Mitchell 2010

Published by
*CT Publications**
40 Higher Bridge Street
Bolton
Greater Manchester
BL1 2HA

Second printing July 2010
 10 9 8 7 6 5 4 3 2

CT Publications is owned by *Chemistry Tutorials* located at the same address.

CONTENTS

1. Be aware of the task you face 5

    What is Synoptic? 5

    Will I have to learn everything? 5

    A Synoptic Carbon Atom 5

    Which Content is Synoptic? 7

  How to use the16:3:3:3 Rule... 8

    Content 8

    Breadth 8

    Relevance 8

    Quality.. 8

2. Scanning a title for clues for effective planning............................... 9

3. Planning to gain marks... 9

  The 50-50 split, examples of these include: 9

  The Short and Sweet type, examples are 10

4. Organising the perfect essay... 11

  Structure 11

  Is it balanced? 11

  Is there a natural organisation? 11

5. What to do if you're stuck... 12

6. Timing 12

  Fleshing out the plan in the last few minutes 12

7. Choosing the right essay for you 13

  Clues in the title... 13

  Trigger words to be wary of in my opinion.. 13

8. Putting it all together 14

APPENDIX 1: AQA's Published Generic Mark Scheme 16

APPENDIX 2: AQA-style Essay Title List.. 19

APPENDIX 3: Suggested essay titles to prepare 20

Disclaimer 21

Essay 01: Ways in which organisms use inorganic ions 22

Essay 02: DNA and information transmission 24

Essay 03: Enzymes and their roles in the functions of cells, tissues and organs 26

Essay 04: The role of the movement of substances across membranes in the function of organs and organ systems 28

Essay 05: Movements within cells 30

Essay 06: Energy transfers within living organisms 32

Essay 07: The structure and function relationhips of proteins 34

Essay 08: Transfers across ecosystems 36

Essay 09: The same parents may produce offspring that differ from each other. Discuss how this is brought about 38

Essay 10: How Carbon dioxide affeccts organisms and ecosystems 40

Essay 11: Describe how the shapes of cells is related to their functions 42

Essay 12: Lipids in health and disease 44

Essay 13: Genes and diversity 46

Essay 14: The physiological impact of lifestyle on health 48

Essay 15: The impact of human activities on the diversity of plants and animals 50

Essay 16: Receptors and their role in coordination 52

Essay 17: The pathways of synthesis of carbohydrates from carbon dioxide 54

Essay 18: Proteins such as insulin, such as insulin, FSH or an anti-influenza antibody are made in cells that are remote from their target tissues. Describe how one of these is synthesised and exerts an effect elsewhere. 56

Essay 19: Perform a critical analysis of the methods used to collect biological data 58

Essay 20: The physiological and ecological effects on organisms of an increase in global temperatures 60

1. BE AWARE OF THE TASK YOU FACE

- ✓ You are expected to construct an essay of between 700 and 1100 words covering a diverse range of synoptic content from the entire A-level specification.
- ✓ Your essay is assessed on a scale (see Appendix 1) marked for content (16 points), breadth (3 points), relevance (3 points) and quality of language (3 points)
- ✓ You will have to select an essay from a choice of 2 titles

WHAT IS SYNOPTIC?

Syn-op-tic [Si-nop-tik] Pertaining or constituting a synopsis; affording or taking a general view of the principal parts of a subject.

This definition comes from *www.dictionary.com* and gives a reasonably good sense of the meaning. Essentially at A-level it can be assumed to mean a focus on key underlying concepts in the subject that are reflected throughout at all levels. So for example in biology, all organisms use ATP to release energy for processes and use proteins as enzymes to control specific reactions. In this context these concepts are deemed to be synoptic and will be covered frequently in questions.

WILL I HAVE TO LEARN EVERYTHING?

Simply put … **NO!** Synoptic questions and essays are not about the regurgitation of every last fine piece of detail, but focus on a DRAWING TOGETHER *OF KEY SYNOPTIC ELEMENTS.* In this book I have identified these elements and provide a process you can easily follow to internalise and consolidate them.

A SYNOPTIC CARBON ATOM

*As a tool to illustrate synoptic thinking I want you to consider a carbon atom, say floating in the air in a CO_2 molecule soaking up infra-red rays in the 1700 cm^{-1} region from the Earth and thereby doing its bit for global warming. Let's follow the fate of this atom and see how many key synoptic elements we can identify (these are highlighted in **bold** for you).*

The infra-red rays strike the **molecule** giving it **kinetic energy** to excite it and make it **move** more rapidly. This allows it to come into close proximity to a leaf of a dandelion plant. Here it **diffuses** through the open stomata down a **concentration gradient** into the air spaces between the mesophyll **cells** and enters the palisade **cell** where it **diffuses** through the **plasma membrane** and through the cytoplasm and on into the stroma of an **organelle** called the chloroplast. Here it is combined to a 5-carbon **sugar**, RuBP, broken down to glycerate-3-phosphate and then gets **reduced** by **hydrogen ions** and **electrons** by a reduced NADP **coenzyme molecule**. Now as an atom in triose phosphate, the **carbon** atom then undergoes a **condensation reaction** to form **glucose**, a **monosaccharide**. The **glucose** it then joined to a fructose to form the

disaccharide sucrose which is **actively transported** into the phloem vessels though a **specific channel protein** using **energy** from the **hydrolysis** of **ATP** to provide **energy** to push it against a concentration **gradient**. This lowers **water potential** allowing **water** to enter the phloem by **osmosis** creating a **hydrostatic pressure** that forces the solution of sugar towards the roots of the dandelion. There it becomes **hydrolysed** to glucose by **enzymes** and **condensed** into a cellulose **polysaccharide** molecule and **assimilated** into the **cell** wall of a root hair **cell**. In doing so, the **carbon** atom is incorporated as part of the plants **biomass** and forms a small part of the **productivity** for the **ecosystem**.

Presently, the dandelion's roots are **consumed** by a **primary consumer** such as a sheep. The sheep swallows the cellulose and the **saprobiotic microorganisms** in its digestive **system** release **enzymes** which **catalyse** the **hydrolysis** of the cellulose into β-glucose. The glucose is **absorbed** through a sodium-glucose co-transporter **protein** through a **specific channel protein** against a concentration **gradient** where it passes into the sheep's **blood**, lowering its **water potential** prompting the release of the **protein hormone** insulin. The insulin and the synoptic carbon atom inside the glucose **molecule** are then **transported** though the blood inside the cardiovascular **system**, down a **pressure gradient** caused by the **contraction** of the ventricles in the sheep's heart. Upon entering a capillary leading into an **organ**, in this case, the liver, the **hydrostatic pressure** forces the glucose, insulin and other small molecules into the **tissues** through the formation of a **tissue** fluid. The insulin **hormone binds** to a **specific complementary receptor** on the **plasma membrane** which opens a **specific** glucose **channel** allowing the glucose to enter the hepatocyte by **facilitated diffusion** across the hydrophobic phospholipid barrier.

Inside the hepatocyte, the glucose becomes **phosphorylated** by **ATP** and undergoes **glycolysis**, being **oxidised** by dehydrogenase **enzymes** to pyruvate. This **diffuses** into the matrix of a mitochondrion, an **organelle**, where it undergoes decarboxylation forming CO_2 (with our synoptic carbon atom) which **diffuses** out though the **lipid bilayer** and ultimately out of the **cell** and through the endothelial cells into the lumen of a capillary. Upon **dissolving** in the **water** of the blood plasma producing HCO_3^- **ions** and, it **diffuses** into a red blood **cell** where it binds to a Fe^{2+} **ion** on a haemoglobin **protein** molecule, unloading **oxygen** in the process at the **exchange surface**. The red blood cell is then **transported** by the beating of the heart to the lungs where the CO_2 **molecule** diffuses off the haemoglobin (as **oxygen** loads in its place) and through the one cell thick epithelium **tissue** of the alveoli into the air in the lungs. **Relaxation** of the intercostal **muscle's** actin and myosin **protein** filaments and the arching of the diaphragm **move** the rib cage down and in, decreasing the volume of the thorax and increasing the **pressure** in the lungs to higher than atmospheric. This creates a pressure **gradient** that forces the CO_2 molecule back though the respiratory **system** and back out into the atmosphere.

Now consider this; we have just written a short synoptic essay! It was about seven hundred or so words covering many synoptic elements. This essay could have been a response to the title ...

Describe the processes by which a carbon atom is transferred between organisms, and between organisms and their environment.

The content covered at least three kingdoms (plants, animals and microorganisms), drawing on content from three modules (e.g. osmosis and carbohydrate and digestion, module 1), photosynthesis and respiration (module 4) and oxygen dissociation and gas exchange (module 2). In the following sections I will describe the precise nature of the synoptic elements covered, and others, and show you a process to follow in order to start to learn them.

WHICH CONTENT IS SYNOPTIC?

Biomolecules

- ✓ A list of biological molecules containing different chemical elements
- ✓ Structure and importance of specific molecules
- ✓ Roles and specific examples of specific molecules

Enzymes

- ✓ Activation energy
- ✓ Generic examples
- ✓ Plant specific
- ✓ Animal specific

Genetic code

- ✓ Structure of DNA
- ✓ Nature of the genetic code
- ✓ Replication
- ✓ Transcription
- ✓ Translation
- ✓ Mutations
- ✓ Roles in differentiation
- ✓ Roles in intra- and inter-specific variation
- ✓ Transfers of genes (horizontal/vertical/sexual)

Cells

- ✓ Plants
- ✓ Animals

Microbes

- ✓ Beneficial roles
- ✓ Harmful roles

Gas exchange

- ✓ Features of gas exchange
- ✓ Surface area to volume ratio good for gas bad for H_2O loss

Movements

- ✓ Diffusion
- ✓ Osmosis
- ✓ Active transport
- ✓ Endocytosis
- ✓ Exocytosis
- ✓ Phagocytosis
- ✓ Hydrostatic pressure
- ✓ Muscle contraction

Energy

- ✓ ATP
- ✓ Heat
- ✓ Light
- ✓ Chemical
- ✓ Photosynthesis
- ✓ Aerobic respiration
- ✓ Anaerobic respiration

Adaptations

- ✓ Xerophytes
- ✓ Behavioural
- ✓ Physiological (haemoglobin etc)
- ✓ Anatomical
- ✓ Gas exchange and cell shapes
- ✓ Natural selection
- ✓ Speciation

Diversity

- ✓ Inter-specific and intra-specific variations
- ✓ Continuous/discontinuous
- ✓ Diversity index
- ✓ Stabilisation of food webs
- ✓ Survival

Coordination/communication

- ✓ Hormonal
- ✓ Nervous
- ✓ Courtship
- ✓ taxes

HOW TO USE THE 16:3:3:3 RULE

The examiners are looking for the following breakdown:

- ✓ 16 Content marks drawn from either specification content or a-level equivalent knowledge.
- ✓ 3 Breadth marks based on either 3 different modules content or 3 different kingdoms of examples.
- ✓ 3 Relevance marks – assume you have them in the bag but lose one each time you make an error.
- ✓ 3 Quality of communication – learn how to use capital letters, full stops and commas appropriately.

CONTENT

The content you include should span at least 5 areas in some detail with two key points and a specific example. So if I was being asked for an importance of ATP, I would state that ... its **hydrolysis by ATPase releases energy** that can be used for **specific** processes, for example **provides energy** for the **active transport** of **mineral ions against a concentration gradient** in a **root hair cell** of a **plant**.

Notice just how many key terms there were in that sentence. These identify it as being high quality for the marker. I could have said ... *ATP is used for active transport of ions in a plant ...* technically the same point but with a much lower quality.

BREADTH

These should be the easiest to gain, just make sure you use examples from at least 3 modules or kingdoms. Remember that most of the examples are animal, fewer plant and hardly any fungi and bacteria ... and most of my students struggle to identify the other kingdom, let alone give examples from it.

But you can collect **generic information** ... by that I mean processes that are common to all living organisms. For example all organisms have a phospholipid bilayer for a membrane that is embedded with channel proteins. So if you were doing an essay on proteins and had very few bacteria examples you could source the membrane channels as an example and illustrate with a bacterial example. E.g. **Protein** molecules can act as **channel** proteins which provide a route by which **hydrophilic** species can pass **through** the **cell membrane**. A **bacteria** such **E. Coli** in the **stomach** of a **mammal** would use these channels to **absorb nutrition** such as **ions** like Na^+, from the **host**.

RELEVANCE

Essentially the only advice here is to keep to the point. In an essay on role of nucleic acids for example, talking about the job of the proteins they code for is off-topic and will **LOSE** you marks. Also common errors like saying DNA is made from polypeptide strands or that DNA is a protein will lose you these marks. **STICK TO THE POINT**.

QUALITY

I should not have to say much here, but quality goes beyond physical sentence construction. Think about the message you are conveying. Lead the reader through a logical sequence. Essays that flit about pointlessly and are incoherent are a nightmare to mark. Plants one minute … animals …plants ….fungi…animals…plant…animal…damn it makes my ears bleed to mark them.

Get an overview of what you are going to write… and use it as a template. Remember the PPPPPP rule … Planning and Preparation Prevents Piss-Poor Performance!

2. SCANNING A TITLE FOR CLUES FOR EFFECTIVE PLANNING

- ✓ Use a **head NOT heart** approach. Do not be drawn into a title you **like** if it not broad enough to gain easy marks. Many essays quickly dry up. For example **"negative feedback and living organisms"** is actually quite limited, even if you feel you can do a reasonable job from that modules content.
- ✓ Essays of the 50-50 type are much more open as they allow a two-pronged attack of the title (see below).
- ✓ Look for any words that allow an expansion of content. For example **"living organisms"** allows you to draw on animals, plants, bacteria, fungi or protoctist examples.

3. PLANNING TO GAIN MARKS

Plan according to the title, carve it up into about 8 by 2 units, or 4 by 4, and then get started!

Previously I showed you broadly how to aim to gain marks with the 16:3:3:3 rule, and now we'll look at the planning stage. Take a look at any synoptic essay title and you'll notice that they fall into two main categories.

THE 50-50 SPLIT, EXAMPLES OF THESE INCLUDE:

- ✓ The structure **and** function relationships of carbohydrates.
- ✓ The causes **and** biological importance of variation.
- ✓ Describe the physiological **and** ecological effects of a rise in global temperatures on living organisms.
- ✓ How are the shapes of cells related **to their** function?

See how each essay can be carved up into a simple split – *something **and** something* or a *relation **to its/their** whatever…* etc

Let's try to carve up the first title, the **Structure and function reltionships of carbohydrates**. On a piece of paper, split the page in two vertically and at the top on the left put structure and on the right, function. Now split the page into eighths so your paper is a grid of **16 boxes**. NOTICE its **16 boxes**! And earlier we saw that we needed **16 content points**. Now in your plan you could fill the boxes in the functions and relate structure to them. For example:

✓ [on right] cellulose cell walls provide strength and support & [on left] long unbranched/polysaccharide/hydrogen bonds/microfibrils
✓ [on right] component of DNA/RNA nucleotides & [on left] monosaccharide/5-Carbon sugar distinguishes DNA from RNA.
✓ [on right] energy storage molecule in plants (starch) & [on left] branched, large amounts of glucose in small volume/easily hydroysed/insoluble.

This process can be repeated until as many of the boxes as possible are filled. Once you have collected something to say on each of the 8 pairs, you can structure and begin the essay.

THE SHORT AND SWEET TYPE, EXAMPLES ARE

✓ Movements **within** cells
✓ Negative feedback **inside** living organisms.
✓ Transfers **through** ecosystems.
✓ Cycles **across** biology.

Notice how these can be recognised by *a process **in/within/through/across/between/inside*** something. At first glance these seem quite daunting, too wide (or too narrow depending how unprepared you are!) I like these as they provide a wide canvas to prepare a plan on.

Let's take say "**Cycles across biology**" Our biology has been studied at a wide number of levels – molecular – cellular – organs – systems – organisms – populations – communities – biotic – abiotic – environmental. Notice there are nine levels here, so aiming for 2 cycles in each would fill our **8×2=16** grid nicely and allow us to start the essay. So, I would move along each level and find a cyclical change. Some levels I may struggle to find any so I would miss it and try to find an extra one elsewhere.

- Molecular – [ATP to ADP and Pi and back] [NAD + 2H$^+$ + 2e$^-$ forming reduced NAD and back]
- Cellular – [The cell cycle] [Krebs] [Calvin]
- Systems -[breathing cycle] [cardiac cycle]
- Organisms – [life cycle] [menstrual cycle]
- Populations – [lag-log-stationary-death-repeat]
- Communities – [predator prey]
- Abiotic -[night-day] [Seasons]
- Environment [Nitrogen] [Carbon cycle] [Energy]
- Gene technology [PCR]

Notice how the simple act of dividing up the essay has broken it down a much easily digestible task and we automatically build in breadth!

The key to the above types of essay is to find that hook, that point that allows you to carve up the roast so as to lever the topic open to gain the breath. There are trigger words in the titles that allow this

✓ **Living organisms** – find examples from animal – plant – fungus – bacteria – protoctist – generic
✓ **Biology** – use the levels I used in the example above
✓ **Cells** – use examples from eukaryotic plant and animals as well as prokaryotic
✓ **Ecosystems** – think abiotic, biotic and trophic levels, also material and energy transfers

So in summary I have shown you how to quickly make a broad plan, an outline for the framework of the essay that uses the title itself to prise open the lid to reveal contents – the meat of the essay.

4. ORGANISING THE PERFECT ESSAY

In the last section I described how to carve up the essay using clues within the title so it became easier to handle and more defined. Now I want to look at developing that theme so that we can add detail and produce an essay that flows and has structure instead of a random series of unconnected sentences.

STRUCTURE

If you have done what I suggested then you will have a piece of paper on which your plan is outlined, but it will be carved up into a series of boxes. It may be that you were unable to find examples to enter for some boxes – that's ok because often more things occur as we proceed with the development of the essay. Now take an objective look at the grid and assess the following:

IS IT BALANCED?

1. By that I mean are there whole sections with nothing in them – if this is the case you must try to think of content to fill them.
2. Try not to keep adding more examples into boxes – your focus MUST be on putting something … anything in as many boxes as possible. Once you have made a point, you will not get any more by using more examples. Common errors include giving about 10 examples of enzymes on a protein importance essay – enzymes are after all, only ONE role of a protein.
3. If you struggle to find specific content, then try to use generic things from biology, like cells, membranes, ATP, proteins, enzymes, respiration, competition, need for nutrition, variation, etc to **force** specific examples. E.g. if I needed a role of a protein in a fungi I can always use a generic example of, say the enzyme ATPase which will hydrolyse ATP to ADP and Pi releasing energy for active transport for mineral ions into a hyphae of a saprobiotic fungus.

IS THERE A NATURAL ORGANISATION?

- ✓ Essays often split into broad **sub-categories** like Animal, Plants etc or Physiological and Ecological effects. Try to find sub-categories to give your essay flow – imagine it a little like blocks stuck together – the **animal** block then the **plant** block then the **other organism** block.
- ✓ Once you identify the sub-categories and have enough boxes filled I suggest you finalise the content and start to write.
- ✓ Use the information from one of your boxes at a time and try to develop it into the following elements. Try to expand the simple statements in the boxes like **NAD** into … **2 key points** … at least **2 specific examples** from the specification where appropriate. So if I was doing Cycles and Biology, and I was in the molecular box, " … *co-enzymes are molecules that work with dehydrogenase enzymes [key point 1]to transfer hydrogen ions and electrons from a substrate during respiration [key point 2] for example NAD accepts 2e⁻ and 2H⁺ from glucose during glycolysis in an animal cell during*

aerobic respiration [specific example 1] and NADP accepts 2e⁻ and 2H⁺ during the light dependent reaction in the thylakoid of a chloroplast in a palisade cell during photosynthesis [specific example 2]. Both of these get re-oxidised when the electrons are passed down an electron transport chain [the cycle bit]"

✓ Always, always, always link the content back to the title of the essay. Avoid falling into the trap of just regurgitating lists of flow charts of content. So if I was doing an essay on *"DNA and information transmission"* I would not just discuss the key points of DNA replication or mitosis, I would link them back to the title first to show the examiner I understood the context. For example, I would put them in a context like ... *"The genetic information encoded in DNA must be transmitted to genetically identical daughter cells when mitosis takes place for growth or repair. To ensure this takes place, the semi-conservative replication of DNA takes place in late interphase of the cell cycle. The enzyme helicase ..."* and then I could include the detail of replication and mitosis safe in the knowledge the context had been made clear.

5. WHAT TO DO IF YOU'RE STUCK

This is a nightmare, you've gotten half way through and you lose the plot a little and dry up! What can you do? Here are a few tips to re-open the essay:

✓ Force yourself to think outside the box, try to come up with any relevant thread you can.
✓ Add extra if you dry up by asking yourself ... **WHY**? or **SO WHAT**? or **TO DO WHAT**? These are great openers!
✓ Go back and add detail, a few words here and there can increase content marks.
✓ Avoid sweeping statements like ... fur is important to animals ... say precisely WHY it is IMPORTANT (if offers a means of camouflage and protection from predators for example) and ask yourself what is the CONSEQUENCE of NOT having it?
✓ Avoid going in too deep – keep to *BREADTH NOT DEPTH*.
✓ Back up every statement with an appropriate example from the syllabus ... don't be shy of using a GCSE example, as its better than nothing.
✓ Avoid lengthy openers or conclusions – these essays are NOT English essays, every word is there for one reason ... to gain marks.

6. TIMING

If you have **16 boxes** and about 35 minutes of writing with 10 minutes planning time it follows you spend about **2 minutes per box**. Remember this – **BREADTH NOT DEPTH** in these essays, go for lots of examples that skate the surface of your biology in a connected way – this is that they are looking for – not loads of fine detail about one or two things!

FLESHING OUT THE PLAN IN THE LAST FEW MINUTES

It may seem odd to discuss adding flesh to the bones of the plan at the end, but it is **VITAL**. The examiners **WILL CREDIT** content that is clearly described in the plan, but only if it has not been included. This is why we did not spend ages planning. Now ... **IN**

THE LAST 5 MINUTES … we go back and add as much clarity and detail to the plan as possible, as these extra marks could be the make or break of our essay.

7. CHOOSING THE RIGHT ESSAY FOR YOU

Let's be clear about what you will face. The essay comes off the back of a big paper and about 15 marks of data handling. You will then face the "open" titles that I've included here and you will have about 45 minutes to write your opus. That's not easy. So now you are faced with a choice of TWO titles. Pick the wrong one and there is not enough time to go back and correct your mistake. So I want to focus on how to choose the right essay for you – and **choose the one with the greatest mark potential**. That should be your **only** criteria. It is important that you are not swayed by personal preferences. Imagine you loved horses and an essay came up … Describe the role of horses in an ecosystem … you'd be over the moon, off you'd go … but really, where to? After you covered eating grass and excreting over a field, I suspect you'd run out of ideas!

I suggest you take an objective look at both titles and try to make a speed plan, a quick carve up of both essay titles. Which has more scope..? Which one can you fill in more boxes for…? Which one has more detail that you know..? Look out for the following:

CLUES IN THE TITLE

Looking at the list of essay titles I included in Appendix 2, the following is a list of triggers in the titles which suggest it can be "opened up" to flood the marks.

- ✓ "Biology" or" Biological": This gives you opportunity to draw from a wide range of levels and/or kingdoms
- ✓ The 50-50 splits offer an easy entry into the carving-up process to start to digest a bigger essay into bite-sized pieces
- ✓ "Living Organisms" offers an easy splitting into animals, plants, fungi, bacteria and protoctists and/or generic examples
- ✓ "Transfer" or "Flow". Think of a movement or flow … FROM…INTO…THROUGH…OUT OF…BETWEEN – again, a nice split to get you thinking.

TRIGGER WORDS TO BE WARY OF IN MY OPINION

- ✓ **"Importance"**. This is hard to get for most people, and I have a simple suggestion for deal with essays with *importance* in the title … **avoid them!**
- ✓ "Negative Feedback" or "Osmosis" any **single narrow topic** – this could soon cause you to **dry up and run out of content** unless you are experienced at forcing examples.
- ✓ "Relationships" e.g. a Structure-fuction *relationships* of protein etc … are do-able but you must take care as you must constantly connect and link the two parts otherwise the content and relevance marks could be very low.

8. PUTTING IT ALL TOGETHER

By definition, I suppose a good essay is one which scores 25/25 marks! If you have followed the tips outlined in the previous section you should be well on the way to generating one. There are some common features of essays that stand out in the examiners eyes and a prior knowledge of these allows them to be built into your essay. In general, a good essay will ...

✓ **Start with a definition of a title keyword.** Definitions show precision and knowledge and demonstrate a good understanding of the content. Starting with one sets the context of the essay and gives a solid entry into the material. For example, if our essay title was PROTEINS AND THEIR IMPORTANCE TO LIVING ORGANISMS, a good definition opener could be ... *Proteins are polymers of amino acids joined by peptide bonds which have a wide variety of key functions in living organisms...*

✓ **Follow up with a statement of intent.** A statement of intent demonstrates a clear focus for the essay and details the objective in a clear and concise manner. Continuing the example above we could now add ... *This essay will list and detail many of these specific roles in plants, animals, fungi and bacteria and highlight the benefits these molecules confer to the organism.*

✓ **Have a clearly discernible structure.** The precise structure will follow from the planning stage and be specific to different essays. Using the example above, it would be logical to follow a sequence of functions through the different kingdoms in turn, separating out those functions that were specific to each, e.g. pancreatic amylase which hydrolyses starch to maltose in the small intestine of an animal would not be mixed with in the same section with penicillinase, an enzyme released by a fungus that hydrolyses cell walls of bacteria.

✓ **Have breadth not depth**. One mistake many students make is to go into a topic in way too much detail. They fail to accept the point at which they scored the marks that were available for the points they are making. When studying the mark schemes of previous essays it becomes clear that only a few key points are required to score marks, but that many topic areas need to be covered. Using the example above, a good essay would cover a few specific examples of many roles for proteins like enzymes, hormones, receptors, fur, channels, antigens, antibodies etc rather than many examples of just hormones or enzymes.

✓ **Show an understanding of the title and not just repeat it.** In essays such as the one above, it is common to find phrases like "... receptors like the insulin receptor have a specific shape to recognise only insulin and so they are a really important role for proteins." This is telling the examiner it is important rather than demonstrating to him you understand why. Instead a phrase " ... the insulin receptor's complementary shape to insulin ensures a cells specific response to the hormone causing the glucose channel to open only when the concentration is high enough."

✓ **Uses specific content from the syllabus.** This should be an obvious point, but a clear demonstration of syllabus specific material will always impress the examiner and targets mark points you know will be there. E.g. The specification lists ... *"Enzymes as catalysts lowering activation energy through the formation of enzyme-substrate complexes."* So in our essay we could stress that ... *"one crucial role for proteins is to act as enzymes. These are protein catalysts that control specific chemical reactions, increasing their rate by lowering the activation energy. This is* *brought about by the formation of an enzyme-substrate complex in which an active site binds to the complementary shaped substrate molecule."*

✓ **Show evidence of extra depth of study**. Try to bring in some examples from the *How Science Works* aspects of the text book or link some content to your genera; knowledge of studies of other subjects. Statements like *"In a recent article in New Scientist it was suggested that … "* will unconsciously help the examiner rate you as someone who has read around the biology and related subjects.

✓ **Uses definitions**. Following on from above, specific definitions of terms will always be a powerful addition to any essay. E.g., *"antibodies are Y-shaped globular proteins secreted by plasma B-cells, with a variable region that targets and binds specific antigens on a pathogen."* … is probably more mark-worthy than "antibodies bind to and inactivate pathogens."

✓ **Contains specific named examples**. Always add quality and flesh to your essay with named examples or enzymes (maltase, DNA polymerase, helicase, etc), hormones (ADH, FSH, insulin etc), animals (seal, lions etc), plants (oak trees, dandelion etc), fungi (bread mould, yeast) .

✓ **Has clear flow and direction**. This type of essay avoids simply being a list. The reader is lead and guided in a planned sequence through the maze of content.

APPENDIX 1: AQA'S PUBLISHED GENERIC MARK SCHEME

A generic mark scheme detailing the general principles by which essays are marked by AQA is available on the BIOL5 specimen paper's mark scheme and can be downloaded free of charge at www.aqa.org.uk. I have included a series of interpretations of this below, and it is advised that you scrutinise the original document and form your own view of the level that is expected of you.

The essay is subdivided into four skill areas that will be marked independently of each other; Scientific content (SC), breadth of knowledge (BOK), relevance to title (RTT) and quality of language (QOL). Students should note that so long as they demonstrate sufficient skill in the areas of BOK, RTT and QOL that they can gain the maximum of 9 marks with very little specific scientific knowledge.

As marking essays is not as clear-cut as marking short answer questions, a series of so-called "descriptors" are used as a basis for marking. The number of descriptors is limited to ensure that there is a suitable difference in quality between the scores. This helps AQA to ensure a greater degree of consistency in the marking.

Scientific content (Maximum 16 marks): You will only be able to score 0, 4, 8, 12 or a maximum of 16 as follows:

Mark	Descriptor
0	The written material is often superficial and is usually inaccurate and provides little evidence of a knowledge that is to be expected from an A-level course.
4	Most of the material is superficial with limited amounts of content being of the required depth. If a greater depth is evidenced, there may be many fundamental errors.
8	There is a significant amount of content that is of an appropriate depth and demonstrates a clear understanding of the principles expected at an A-level course. Most of the content will be accurate and is presented with few fundamental errors.
12	Most of the written content is of a high standard and demonstrates a clear understanding of the underlying principles. The material has no fundamental errors within it, although there may be some minor errors that lower the overall accuracy of the essay.
16	The entire material is accurate and of a high standard throughout the essay. There are also some links of references to material that provides evidence for a greater breadth depth, or range of study.

"When marking the essay, it will be categorised into GOOD, AVERAGE or POOR. It is important therefore that the material you select ensures it is classed as Good."

A **good** essay is one that

- includes a sufficient level of detail that is expected from a comprehensive knowledge and understanding of relevant parts of the specification
- demonstrates an appropriate depth and accuracy throughout
- avoids basic and fundamental errors
- covers a majority of the key areas that might be expected from the title of the essay.
- Clearly demonstrates the links between principles and ideas from different topic areas.

An **average** essay is one that

- A level of content that might be expected of grade C - E candidates
- is likely to have less detail and be more patchy in the depth to which areas are covered, and may omit several important and relevant areas
- is likely to include some errors and misunderstandings, but should have few basic errors
- is likely to include mainly more superficial and less clear-cut connections

A **poor** essay is one that

- is largely below the standard expected of a grade E candidate
- shows very limited knowledge and understanding of the topic
- is likely to cover only very few relevant areas and may be relatively short
- is likely to provide superficial treatment of connections
- includes many errors, including some major ones

Breadth of knowledge (maximum 3 marks)

Mark	Descriptor
0	Material mostly irrelevant.
1	Almost all of the material focuses on a single topic area.
2	A number of areas are covered by there is a lack of balance and some key areas are missing.
3	A balanced account that covers most of the key topic areas expected from a from an A-level study course.

"So for BOK, always cover a number of areas in detail, focussing on the most important, and give each of the concepts approximately equal weighting in your account."

Relevance (maximum 3 marks)

Mark	Descriptor
0	Material entirely irrelevant or there is too little to mark.
1	A major portion of the essay is irrelevant although some attempt has been made to link to the title.
2	The selected material is generally relevant to the title but much of the main content is of only marginal relevance.
3	All the material presented is relevant to the title.

"So for RTT, always cover areas that are relevant to the title and constantly link back to it in order to stay on track."

Quality of language (maximum 3 marks)

Mark	Descriptor
0	Material mostly irrelevant or there is too little to mark.
1	The essay is poorly constructed and there is usually a lack of appropriate scientific style and terminology.
2	The essay is presented in a logical sequence with presentation in clear scientific English. Scientific terminology is generally accurate and used appropriately and accurately.
3	The material is presented in clear scientific English and the scientific terminology is used accurately and effectively throughout the essay.

"So for QOL, always present your material using the correct scientific terminology. Always present your ideas in a clear and logical flow."

In summary, examiners will be looking out are looking for ...

1. evidence of knowledge and understanding that is of an appropriate depth to A level study
2. choice of relevant content from different areas of the specification
3. treatment of the main ideas and principles that might be expected in relation to the essay title
4. connection of ideas, principles and other information from different areas in response to the specific essay title
5. production of an account that forms a flowing and logical response
6. clear and logical expression, using accurate scientific vocabulary appropriate to A level study

APPENDIX 2: AQA-STYLE ESSAY TITLE LIST

I have included below a list of titles that are similar to those used by AQA in the legacy specifications A and B. AQA currently have examples of these legacy papers and are available online free of charge at *www.aqa.org.uk*. You need to take care not to assume that these are entirely reflective of the new specification, but they offer a clear picture of the scope and styles the essays will take.

Biology
- Cycles and Biology
- Negative feedback within living organisms
- The physiological and ecological effects on organisms of an increase in global temperatures
- DNA and information transmission

Biolmolecules
- The ways in which organism use ATP
- The importance of water in biology
- The structures and functions of different carbohydrates
- The structures and functions of different proteins
- Describe how inorganic ions are used by living organisms
- The structures and functions of polymers in biology
- How carbon dioxide affects organisms and ecosystems
- Enzymes and their roles in the functions of cells, tissues and organs

Cells
- The structure to function relationship of cells
- The ways in which bacteria affect human lives
- How is the shape of cells related to their functions?

Transport
- The movements of materials within living organisms
- Movement of carbon dioxide out of an organism from a respiring cell
- The biological importance of osmosis
- Movements of carbon-containing substances between organisms and organisms and their environment
- Movements within cells
- Transfers across ecosystems
- The role of movement of substances across membranes in the function of organs and systems

Energy
- Energy transfers between organisms and between organisms and their environment
- Energy transfers within living organisms

Diversity
- Causes of biological variation and its importance
- The ways in which species or organism differ from each other
- The same parents may produce offspring that differ from each other. Discuss how this is brought about.

APPENDIX 3: SUGGESTED ESSAY TITLES TO PREPARE

I've included a list of possible titles which I think reflect the changes of direction within the new A level. Each one is very synoptic and covers a wide range of topics from AS and A2.

1. Lipids in health and disease.
2. The physiological basis of disease
3. Genes and diversity.
4. The ways in which different organisms become adapted to their environments.
5. Coordination within organisms and between organisms and their environments.
6. Discuss how scientists collect, analyse and interpret biological data.
7. A space probe brought back samples of life-forms from a hot, dry planet with low atmospheric oxygen but high carbon dioxide concentrations. Describe the adaptations these life-forms would have in order to survive these conditions.
8. The physiological impact of lifestyle on health.
9. The impact of human activities on the diversity of animals and plants.
10. Receptors and their roles in coordination.
11. The pathways of synthesis of carbohydrates from atmospheric carbon dioxide.
12. Proteins such as insulin, FSH or an anti-influenza antibody are made in cells that are remote from their target tissues. Describe how one of these is synthesised and exerts an effect elsewhere.
13. Perform a critical analysis of methods used to collect biological data.
14. Stem cells research offers a great number of potential benefits to humans. It also comes with many down sides. Write a balanced account of the ways in which stem cells could and should be used to benefit humans.
15. Discuss the benefits and drawbacks of gene cloning technologies.

DISCLAIMER

The essays included in this work by no means represent the only possible answers to the examination-style questions. By its very nature, synoptic biology covers a wide range of topics, many of which would also be relevant to some of the titles. These essays are provided only as a means to guide students on the length, composition, style and quality that they should strive to achieve in their own essays. Essay titles that are similar to those asked in the legacy specifications A and B have been included where the content is clearly relevant to the new specification.

While every effort has been made to match the content included to previously published AQA mark schemes, where available, there may be instances where individual examiners would not award the full 25 marks to some of the essays. The essays included here are not endorsed in any way by AQA but are the work of the author. It is the author's belief that based on extensive teaching and marking experience, each essay contains sufficient relevant material from the new AQA specification to score 25/25.

ESSAY 01: WAYS IN WHICH ORGANISMS USE INORGANIC IONS

Inorganic ions are charged particles that do not contain carbon atoms bonded together. While organisms are mainly built from carbon-containing molecules, their functions rely on inorganic ions such as nitrate, hydrogen and calcium. This essay will detail some of the roles of specific ions and describe how animals, plants and bacteria use them.

Productivity in an ecosystem in the soil is limited in part by the availability of fixed nitrogen in the soil. Nitrogen fixing bacteria in the roots of leguminous plants reduce atmospheric nitrogen to ammonium using ATP and reduced NAD. The ammonium ions released into the soil are oxidised by nitrifying bacteria firstly to nitrite, and then to nitrate. This oxidation increases the nitrogen content in the soil which plants can use to produces many useful molecules including amino acids, proteins, DNA and ATP. The formation of these ions forms part of the ecological nitrogen cycle which plays a key role in sustaining life on this planet.

Plants are the producers for an ecosystem. They photosynthesise carbon dioxide and water and produce energy in the form of carbohydrates and other molecules. Photosynthesis requires water, and plants gain water from the soil using mineral ions such as nitrate produced by the nitrifying bacteria. Hydrolysis of ATP releases energy for processes such as active transport of the nitrate ions (and others such as potassium etc) from the soil into root hair cells, a process that lowers water potential and is used to draw water into the plant from the soil. In leaves, photosynthesis involves the photolysis of water, a process that involves the attachment of two electrons to a magnesium ion in chlorophyll and the production of hydrogen ions from the breakdown of water. Together with the electrons, the hydrogen ions are used to reduce NADP in the light-dependent reaction in the thylakoid. The hydrogen ions and electrons in turn are used to reduce glycerate-3-phosphate to form triose phosphate and glucose. Hydrogen ions also play a role in the production of ATP in the electron transport chains. They are pumped into the inter-membrane space and generate an electrochemical gradient that provides energy for the activation of ATPase which combines ADP and inorganic phosphate ions to form ATP.

The glucose, proteins and other molecules produced by the plants can then be consumed by animals for use in their life processes. The glucose undergoes respiration in cells in three different stages, each involving inorganic ions. On hydrolysis, ATP releases energy and a phosphate ion which can be used to phosphorylate glucose in the cell cytoplasm during its glycolysis. This phosphorylation makes the glucose more reactive and prevents it from leaving the cell. Following the transfer of hydrogen ions to coenzymes such as NAD, the pyruvate formed enters the mitochondrion and is decarboxylated and oxidised, in the process transferring its hydrogen ions and electrons to NAD and FAD. These hydrogen ions are pumped into the inter-membrane spaces of the cristae and are used to create an electrochemical gradient to form ATP as part of oxidative phosphorylation.

On role of The ATP produced is in the formation of a resting potential in nerve cells. Hydrolysis of ATP provides energy that is used to pump out three sodium ions and pump in two potassium ions into the axon of a neurone through a specific cation pump by active transport. A reduction of the membrane permeability to sodium ions maintains a resting potential of -70mV on the inside of the axon. Generation of an action potential also uses the charges from ions. Sodium gated channels open in the axon membrane allowing sodium ions to enter. This causes the membrane to depolarise until the threshold voltage of +40mV opens potassium gated channels. This causes potassium ions to leave repolarising, and eventually hyperpolarising the cell. This wave of depolarisation caused by these ion movements allows the passage of nerve impulse and coordination of the animal within its environment, allowing it to move sense and move effectively.

This movement involves the contraction of muscles, another process that uses ions, this time calcium. Calcium ions bind to tropnin, which causes tropomyosin to move away from the myosin head binding site on actin filaments. Once an actomyosin cross-bridge is formed and the actin filament slides into myosin, calcium ions activate ATPase to hydrolyse ATP to ADP and phosphate ions, a process that releases energy for the detachment and reformation of cross bridges. Contraction of the muscle sarcomere allows the contraction of skeletal muscle, allowing the animal to move. Muscles contractions are also used by animals in processes such as controlling light entry into the eye blood flow in arterioles in maintenance of homeostasis. All these processes require nervous coordination and contraction, emphasising the importance of the inorganic ions for proper function.

Contraction of intercostals muscles allows ventilation of the lungs to take place in mammals. This introduces oxygen to the gas exchange surface, the epithelium of the alveoli of the lungs. In order to maintain a high concentration gradient, the oxygen is rapidly removed, a process involving another mineral ion, iron. Iron 3+ ions are attached to haem groups on haemoglobin inside red blood cells. The iron can form bonds to oxygen, allowing haemoglobin to load oxygen in the lungs when the partial pressure of oxygen is high. Each molecule of haemoglobin can bind four oxygen molecules allowing a rapid saturation and the production of oxyhaemoglobin. On contraction of the ventricles, the pressure forces the red blood cells through the body to regions where the partial pressure of oxygen is lower. Here, the haemoglobin unloads, making oxygen available for aerobic respiration and the production of ATP.

In summary, inorganic ions are used in a diverse range of functions in living organisms. This essay has described some of these roles learned during the a-level study and has stressed their key importance in the life processes of bacteria, plants and animals.

ESSAY 02: DNA AND INFORMATION TRANSMISSION

Deoxyribonucleic acid, DNA, carries the genetic code for all living organisms on this planet. It is variation in the information it carries in form of genes and alleles that produces the wide diversity of life, and the variations within and between species. This essay will describe the structure of DNA and illustrate the ways in which the information encoded within it is transmitted within a cell, and between cells and organisms.

DNA is a polymer, a double helix of two polynucleotide strands bonded together by hydrogen bonds. Each nucleotide comprises of a phosphate group attached to a five carbon deoxyribose sugar and an organic base containing nitrogen. These bases can be either adenine (A), thymine (T), cytosine (C) or guanine (G). Adjacent nucleotides are joined by a condensation reaction to form the phosphate-sugar backbone of a polynucleotide strand. Two complementary strands then join by specific base pairing (A to T, C to G), which then wind together to form the double helix which provides strength and stability to the molecule.

The information in DNA is encoded in the sequence of bases along the template strand of the DNA. A gene is a sequence of bases on DNA that codes for the sequence of amino acids in a polypeptide chain. Since proteins determine the functions and structures of cells, it is the DNA code that controls all cellular activities. Organisms of the same species carry the same genes at fixed positions, called loci, but individuals carry different slightly different versions, termed alleles. Variation in these alleles results in intraspecific variation within a species, such as blood groups, eye colour etc.

In order for the genetic material to be transferred into daughter cells as the organism grows or repairs, the DNA must be replicated by semi-conservative replication. The enzyme, helicase binds to the DNA breaking the hydrogen bonds allowing the exposed bases on the two template strands to be revealed. DNA-nucleotides then bind to exposed bases by specific base pairing with hydrogen bonds. DNA polymerase then joins adjacent nucleotides with a condensation reaction forming the phosphate-sugar backbone. Each of the two new DNA molecules formed each contains one of the original strands of DNA. In this way the replication is semi-conservative and helps to minimise the incidence of mistakes, termed mutations, in the copying of the code.

In prokaryotic cells the DNA is free in the cell cytoplasm, but in eukaryotes it is bound within a nucleus and joined to structural proteins, called histones. The structure formed is called a chromosome and it is these that must be separated for the daughter cells to carry the same genetic information as the parent cell.

The process of mitosis separates the two copies of each chromosome. During prophase the chromosomes coil up and become visible, the nuclear envelope disappears and the chromosomes attach to spindle fibres at the equator of the cell using their centromere in metaphase. In anaphase the centromere divides and the spindle contracts drawing the chromatids to opposite poles of the cell. After telophase and cytokineis, two new daughters are formed, each containing an identical copy of the DNA code; hence the encoded information has been transmitted vertically. Bacteria also possess the ability to transmit some of their genes horizontally. Conjugation tubes can form between two bacterial cells and the plasmid, small loops of DNA that carry codes for antibiotic resistance, can pass between the two cells. So if one bacteria owns has a plasmid that carries the code for penicilinase, the plasmid can be replicated and passed via conjugation to another. Now both cells are resistant to penicillin.

The information on DNA is encoded as triplets of bases, called codons. Each triplet can code for one amino acid in a polypeptide chain. So for example, if GCA codes for the amino acid alanine and TAC codes for glycine, then the code GCAGCATACGCA would code for a polypeptide with the sequence ala-ala-gly-ala. As there are over twenty different amino acids in nature, a triplet code allows coding of up to 64 amino acids. Such a code is termed redundant and in reality each amino acid is coded for by several different codes. This minimises mutation rates as, for example, if GCC also codes for alanine, then a mutation from CA to CC would have no effect on primary structure. Each of the codons is translated in sequence as the code is non-overlapping, but first the genetic information must be transcribed, and then transferred out of the nucleus. It is transferred as an RNA molecule, a single-stranded polynucleotide containing the base uracil instead of thymine, and the five-carbon sugar ribose.

Transcription produces a copy of a gene in the form of messenger RNA (mRNA). Helicase binds to the gene locus causing DNA to unwind and reveal a template strand. RNA-nucleotides bind by specific base pairing and RNA polymerase joins them by condensation to form a strand of pre-mRNA. Introns (non-coding regions) are then removed and the exons (coding regions) are spliced together with enzymes to form the mRNA which is small enough to diffuse through the nuclear pore and bind to a ribosome on the rough endoplasmic reticulum.

The process of protein synthesis, or translation can now begin. In the cytoplasm, a transfer RNA (tRNA) molecule binds to a specific amino acid and two such complexes deliver their amino acids to the ribosome. The anticodon on tRNA binds to the complementary codon on mRNA by specific base pairing (A to U, C to G). An enzyme now forms the peptide bind between the amino acids by condensation using energy from ATP and the process is repeated building up the polypeptide chain. Alterations of the base sequence of the gene, mutations alter the structure of the mRNA and so possibly altering the primary structure of the polypeptide coded for. These can be substitutions, deletions of additions. The greatest corruption of the code occurs with the latter two which cause frame shifts that are catastrophic to the base sequence and the primary structure of the coded protein.

Sexually reproducing organisms transmit their genes in the form of haploid gametes (ova and sperm, or pollen) formed by meiosis. This reductive cell division halves the chromosome number so the diploid number of chromosomes can be regenerated on fertilisation. Meiosis introduces variation through crossing over and independent segregation of chromosomes, and random fusion ensures further variety in the offspring produced. In this way the genetic information is transmitted from generation to generation introducing a diverse range of alleles that adds not only variety, but helps ensure a population can survive and adapt to any environmental changes.

ESSAY 03: ENZYMES AND THEIR ROLES IN THE FUNCTIONS OF CELLS, TISSUES AND ORGANS

Enzymes are biological catalysts that control almost all chemical reactions inside and outside cells. In this way they control the functions of not only individual cells, but of collections of cells (tissues), or collections of tissues (organs). This essay will demonstrate the diverse range of ways enzymes contribute to the functioning of these structures.

Enzymes are globular proteins which have a specific tertiary structure that has a complementary shape to that of a specific substrate molecule. The lock and key model is used to describe enzyme action. For example the enzyme lactase has an active site (a lock) that is complementary only to lactose (the key). Sucrose, a similar disaccharide has a different shape to lactose and so cannot bind to lactase's active site. On binding to the active site, an enzyme-substrate complex is formed and reaction takes place. The products have a different shape and can no longer remain bound. In the induced fit model, the active site is not complementary to the substrate, but on binding the shape changes and the active site forms, molding itself to the substrate a tight glove would mould to a hand.

Humans gain the molecular building blocks they need for energy and growth from digestion of food by the digestive system. This is a system of organs that is adapted for the hydrolysis of food molecules and the absorption of their products. In the mouth, the enzyme amylase in the saliva hydrolyses starch to the disaccharide maltose, which is further digested in the intestinal epithelium to α-glucose. In the stomach endopeptidases such as pepsin break down proteins in smaller peptides, and exopeptidases such as trypsin further hydrolyse these into amino acids in the small intestine. Glucose is then absorbed by sodium-glucose transport, a type of active transport that involves the enzyme ATPase which hydrolyses ATP to ADP and Pi releasing energy to pump sodium ions out, and potassium into epithelial cells creating diffusion gradient for sodium and glucose uptake. Enzymes also play a key role in digestion of large insoluble food molecules into smaller, more soluble products that can be transported and assimilated in fungi and bacteria. Decomposers in the ecosystem, the fungi and bacteria, release hydrolytic enzymes such as lipase, carbohydrase and protease (to digest triglycerides, carbohydrates and proteins respectively). The soluble products of this extracellular digestion (e.g. fatty acids, glucose, and amino acids) can then be absorbed and assimilated into useful compounds.

All organisms carry the genetic code for their functions as a DNA molecule. Before a cell divides by mitosis, the DNA must undergo semi-conservative replication to produce two identical copies for the daughter cells. Enzymes play a key role here. Helicase binds to the DNA, breaking the hydrogen bonds that hold the two polynucleotide chains together. This reveals two template strands which have exposed bases which bind to DNA-nucleotides. A second enzyme, DNA polymerase then forms a phosphate-sugar backbone by joining adjacent nucleotides with a condensation reaction.

Some cells, such as β-cells of the pancreas synthesise and secrete protein hormones such as insulin. In order for the genetic code on DNA to be expressed and the insulin formed, the DNA must be transcribed as a pre-mRNA molecule, spliced to form mRNA and transcribed as a protein. Enzymes are involved in each step. Helicase binds to the gene locus and cause the gene to unwind exposing the template strand. RNA polymerase joins adjacent nucleotides in a condensation reaction to form the pre-mRNA strand. Enzymes in the nucleus remove non-coding introns, and splice together the coding exons leading to the formation of an active mRNA which binds to a ribosome on the rough endoplasmic reticulum. Transfer RNA complexes line up with their anticodons on the codons on mRNA and bring two amino acids in contact with an enzyme in the ribosome that condenses them together by forming a peptide bond. The process is repeated to build up the primary structure of the insulin molecule. The action of the hormone insulin also involves phosphorylase enzymes which cause the condensation of glucose molecules into the storage polysaccharide glycogen in the liver by glycogenesis.

All living cells release the energy in substrate molecules using aerobic or anaerobic respiration. The respiratory process is a sequence of interconnected enzyme controlled steps called a metabolic pathway. Other pathways include photosynthesis and the synthesis of steroid hormones such as oestrogen from cholesterol. During glycolysis, the link reaction and the Krebs cycle, some of the steps include oxidation by dehydrogenase enzymes. This oxidation involves the transfer of hydrogen ions and electrons from the substrate and passing them to a coenzyme which becomes reduced. For example, in the cytoplasm, when triose phosphate molecules are oxidised to pyruvate as part of glycolysis, the coenzyme NAD is reduced forming reduced NAD. The coenzyme forms part of the active site of the dehydrogenase enzyme allowing it to function as a catalyst and be reformed.

The ATP formed as part of respiration is used in a wide variety of contexts in biology. For example in order for an animal to move and hunt for food within its environment, it has to contract its muscle tissue. The tissue is composed of cells containing actin and myosin filaments which move relative to each other to contract a sarcomere. For this to happen, actomyosin cross-bridges form between the actin and myosin. Once activated by calcium ions, the enzyme ATPase then hydrolyses ATP to ADP and Pi releasing energy for the detachment and formation of more cross-bridges, giving rise to the sliding filament theory of muscle contraction. This enzyme also helps release energy from ATP in a wide variety of contexts, such as in the active transport of sodium ions out of an axon through sodium-potassium cation pump in the generation of a resting potential, or in the active transport of nitrate ions into a root hair cell to lower water potential to draw in water to generate a root pressure.

This essay has established that enzymes are fundamental biological molecules which offer a diverse range of functions to living organisms.

ESSAY 04: THE ROLE OF THE MOVEMENT OF SUBSTANCES ACROSS MEMBRANES IN THE FUNCTION OF ORGANS AND ORGAN SYSTEMS

Organ systems are collections of organs that work together to perform a common function. Often the function of these organs requires the movements of materials across the membranes of the cells of which they are composed. This essay will describe the part played by the movement of specific substance in the functions of different organs and organ systems.

The cell surface membrane is a plasma membrane composed of a phospholipid bilayer. It acts as a hydrophobic barrier that prevents the passive diffusion of hydrophilic species such as glucose and amino acids into the cell. Hydrophilic channel proteins are embedded in the bilayer which provides a route by which polar substances can enter, either down a concentration gradient by facilitated diffusion or against a concentration gradient by active transport. The relative movements of the lipid molecules together with the random arrangement proteins give rise to the term the *fluid mosaic model* of the cell surface membrane.

Non-polar molecules such as fatty acids, oxygen and carbon dioxide are able to dissolve directly through the membrane and enter the cell by diffusion. This process is used in the lungs whose function is the gas exchange of carbon dioxide and oxygen across the epithelium of the alveoli. Contraction of the intercostal muscles and the flattening of the diaphragm move the rib cage up and out, increasing the volume of the thorax. This decreases the pressure allowing air to be drawn into the lungs down a pressure gradient. This ventilates the epithelial cells of the alveoli allowing oxygen to diffuse through the membrane through the cells. The oxygen then continues to diffuse through the membrane of the red blood cells where it loads to haemoglobin forming oxyhaemoglobin. The carbon dioxide follows the reverse route and is expelled from the lungs during expiration as the intercostal muscles relax.

The oxygen helps cells to release energy as ATP during aerobic respiration. The oxygen helps to increase the permeability of the mitochondrial membrane allowing pyruvate formed in glycolysis to enter the matrix of the mitochondrion. The reduced NAD also formed passes its electrons down an electron transport chain in a series of redox reactions from one carrier molecule to the next. In doing so it increases the permeability of channel protein the inner membrane to hydrogen ions, which then pass into the inter-membrane space. This lowers the pH and helps to generate an electrochemical gradient which activates ATPase to combine ADP and Pi to form ATP.

All organisms use ATP as an immediate energy source for processes such as active transport. In plants, the roots are an organ system whose purpose is the uptake of mineral ions and water, and its movement though to the endodermis and xylem via the apoplast and symplast pathways. The root hair cells have specific channels for ions such as nitrate and potassium. These channels have the enzyme ATPase which hydrolyses ATP and releases energy to absorb the ions against a concentration gradient into the cell. This movement into the cell from the soil lowers the water potential of the roots hair cells allowing water to enter by osmosis. Movement of this water then takes place via the symplast pathways (through cell cytoplasm) and apoplast pathways (via gaps in the cell walls). Water crosses the junctions of adjacent cells through plasmodesmata, small gaps that allow its smooth passage to the endodermis. Active transport of the mineral ions into the xylem allows the water to enter the xylem by osmosis generating a hydrostatic pressure called the root pressure. This creates a push, which together with the cohesion-tension pulls water up the xylem in a column through the hollow lignified xylem vessels.

Animals use an excretory system to remove any waste products such as urea. The role of one key organ, the kidney, is to form a more concentrated urine and reabsorb glucose, sodium ions and water while excluding the urea. The membranes of the kidney tubules are adapted to allow this function. The narrowing of the afferent arteriole generates a hydrostatic pressure at the glomerulus which forces blood against the capillary network. Water and small molecules pass through the pores while proteins and cells are excluded by the process of ultrafiltration. These smaller molecules enter the Bowman's capsule and the proximal convoluted tubule, which has many sodium and glucose channels. These allow the selective reabsorption of these materials into the surrounding tissues. This lowers the water potential so water moves out of the tubule by osmosis and is reabsorbed with the ions into the capillaries that surround the tubules. As the membrane does not have channels for urea, urea remains in the tubule increasing in concentration. The ascending limb of the loop of Henle is impermeable to water. Sodium and chloride ions are actively transported out onto the surrounding tissues through a specific channel using ATP. This lowers water potential creating a water potential gradient that draws water from the descending limb by osmosis. This counter current multiplier further contributes to the reabsorption of water, one of the key functions of the kidney. A protein hormone, ADH is released by the pituitary gland and binds to specific receptors on the collecting ducts of the kidney in situations when the blood water potential is too low. This increases the membranes permeability to water effectively increasing the volume reabsorbed at the same time decreasing the volume of urine produced

One example of the consequences of uncontrolled ions movements is when the bacterium, *Vibrio cholerae* releases its toxin in the large intestine. The protein binds to and opens a chloride ion channels on the epithelium surface. Chloride ions flood out into the lumen lowering water potential causing rapid loss of water, chronic diarrhoea and severe dehydration. In the absence of the toxin these ions would have remained inside the epithelial cells. Water alone cannot be used to rehydrate the sufferer as it cannot easily be absorbed through the intestinal epithelium. The reabsorption of water requires sodium and glucose, two key components of oral rehydration solutions. These species are taken up by co-transport in the small intestine region of the digestive system which lowers water potential sufficiently to allow the absorption of water and the rehydration of the sufferer.

This essay has highlighted how the movements of substances across cell membranes contributes to the functions of the root systems in plants, and the digestive and excretory systems of animals.

ESSAY 05: MOVEMENTS WITHIN CELLS

Cells are the simplest living unit of which all organisms are composed. They are bounded by a phospholipid bilayer through which materials must pass, and many organelles such as mitochondria (which produce energy in the form of ATP) and ribosomes (the site of protein synthesis). The cell's functions rely on the efficient movement of substances into, through and out of, the cell. This essay will detail some of these movements emphasising how the movement is brought about.

For a cell to function, glucose must enter to supply substrate for respiration. Glucose is a hydrophilic monosaccharide and cannot therefore diffuse directly through the hydrophobic membrane. Specific extrinsic glucose channel proteins have a complementary shape that allows glucose to enter the cytoplasm by facilitated diffusion down a concentration gradient. In contrast, hydrophobic substances such as fatty acids are able to diffuse directly through the bilayer. Plant cells such as root hair cells use active transport to take up mineral ions such as nitrate and potassium ions from the soil against a concentration gradient. The energy for this process is supplied by the hydrolysis of ATP using the enzyme ATPase and a specific protein channel in the membrane.

Respiration of the glucose to form ATP involves the movements of many substances. Glucose diffuses through the cytoplasm and is converted by oxidation in a metabolic pathway to pyruvate, a substance which then diffuses through the mitochondrial membrane into its matrix. Here, it undergoes both the link reaction and the Krebs cycle producing reduced coenzymes, reduced NAD and FAD. These then diffuse to the cristae where they pass their electrons down an electron transport chain in a series of redox reactions. Part of this process involves the movement of hydrogen ions into the inter-membrane space to generate an electrochemical gradient to provide energy for the production of ATP.

ATP plays another role in the movements of actin filaments in a mammal's muscle cells. For a sarcomere to contract, an actin fibre must move into a myosin filament (the sliding filament theory). Calcium ions bind to troponin causing the removal of tropomyosin from the myosin head binding site on the filament. The myosin head can attach to form an actomyosin cross-bridge that "nods" to the left drawing actin into myosin. Calcium ions activate ATPase to hydrolyse ATP to ADP and Pi to provide energy for the further detachment and reformation of cross-bridges, in this way contracting the length of the sarcomere and muscle fibre allowing movement of the animal.

All cell's functions are controlled in the nucleus by DNA. The DNA is attached to structures called chromosomes which are too large to pass through the nuclear pores into the cytoplasm where the ribosomes can translate the genetic code and synthesise proteins. Through the process of transcription, a molecule of messenger RNA (mRNA) is created that is a complementary copy of a gene. This is small enough to diffuse out through the pores and bind to the ribosomes on the rough endoplasmic reticulum situated outside the nucleus. In the cytoplasm, amino acids are joined to their specific transfer RNA (tRNA) and are carried inside the ribosome where the anticodon on tRNA can bind to the complementary codon on mRNA by specific base pairing. An enzyme then joins adjacent amino acids forming a peptide bond by a condensation reaction. In this way a protein's primary structure is built up. Once completed, the finished polypeptide is diffused though the smooth ER to the golgi apparatus where the specific three dimensional tertiary structure is put in place through the production of disulphide bridges, ionic bonds etc. The finished protein is packaged into a vesicle that "pinches" off from the golgi and awaits secretion from the cell by exocytosis.

Before a cell can replicate, the DNA must be replicated by semi-conservative replication, in the phase of the cell cycle referred to as late interphase. Helicase binds to DNA breaking the hydrogen bonds between the polynucleotide strands revealing two template strands. DNA nucleotides line up on each strand (adenine with thymine and cytosine with guanine) and DNA polymerase joins adjacent nucleotides by a condensation reaction. Each new DNA molecule produced carries one of the strands from the original DNA thus conserving the genetic code. For cell replication to occur by mitosis, the replicated chromosomes must pass out of the nucleus and attach to spindle fibres at the cell's equator. During prophase, the nuclear membrane disintegrates and the chromosomes coil up and become visible. Since there is now nothing to stop the DNA's movement, the chromosomes move to the equator and attach to the spindle fibres using their centromeres. In metaphase, all the chromosomes are aligned at the equator. During anaphase, the centromeres then split and the spindles contract, pulling the sister chromatids to opposite poles of the cell. In this way each pole of the cell now has a full set of chromosomes and so telophase can occur to reform the nuclear envelopes. Following the splitting of the cytoplasm by cytokinesis, two new cells have been formed, each with a full complement of chromosomes.

In plants water is moved up the xylem through xylem vessels that are hollow. The functions of these cells include transporting water and mineral ions up the plant from the roots and provide support. They are dead cells that have lignified walls providing strength and support. The water is pushed upwards via a root pressure. The active transport of mineral ions from the endodermis into the xylem lowers the water potential, allowing water to enter by osmosis. This creates the hydrostatic pressure, called root pressure, which pushes water up the plant through the hollow xylem vessels. Water is also pulled up by the cohesion-tension mechanism. Evaporation of water from mesophyll cells creates a water potential gradient (a tension) that draws water from the xylem to replace that which was lost. Adjacent water molecules have a weak inter molecular force called a hydrogen bond (a cohesion) between them, so as one molecule is drawn through the cells, the next follows pulling water through the xylem vessels in a column.

ESSAY 06: ENERGY TRANSFERS WITHIN LIVING ORGANISMS

All living organisms such as plants and animals require energy to power their cellular processes. This energy may be in the form of the molecule ATP, or as heat. This essay will detail the processes by which energy is transferred inside organisms and discuss how these transfers are utilised.

In biological processes, the immediate energy source is often in the form adenosine triphosphate (ATP). ATP is readily hydrolysed by the enzyme ATPase to ADP and Pi (inorganic phosphate ions). This hydrolysis releases a packet of energy of approximately 31 $kJmol^{-1}$ which can be used to provide energy for processes such as muscle contraction, the generation of nerve impulses or active transport.

Plants are able to produce ATP during the light dependent reaction of photosynthesis in the thylakoid of the chloroplast. Red and blue wavelengths of light are absorbed by chlorophyll on Photosystem II. The energy absorbed is transferred to electrons and excites them to a higher energy level. This stimulates photolysis of water which results in the formation of hydrogen ions, electrons and oxygen gas. The electrons formed during photolysis then replace those excited by the light. The excited electrons are then passed along an electron transport chain in a series of redox reactions from one carrier to the next. The energy released by this passage is used to activate ATPase to combine ADP and Pi to form ATP. In this way one can consider the energy in light as being transferred to the ATP. The hydrogen ions released by photolysis are used to reduce NADP. The ATP and reduced NADP are then used for the reduction of glycerate-3-phosphate to triose phosphate in the light independent reaction in the stroma of the chloroplast. This triose phosphate can then be used to form glucose (which can be used as a substrate for respiration), stored as starch (an insoluble energy store in leaves or tubers) or incorporated into the other plant tissues.

The glucose or starch can be used as an energy source directly by the plants, or indirectly by animals which consume, digest, absorb and assimilate the sugars. Glucose, a six carbon monosaccharide, is a commonly used respiratory substrate in, for example by intestinal epithelial cells in animals to provide energy for sodium-glucose co-transport. The glucose enters the cell through a specific protein channel by facilitated diffusion, down a concentration gradient using only kinetic energy provided by heat. In the cytoplasm each glucose is phosphorylated by two molecules of ATP effectively transferring energy to make it more reactive. The fructose bisphosphate formed is then cleaved and oxidised to release 4 ATP (giving a net gain of 2 molecules). Each molecule of glucose forms two molecules of pyruvate and two of reduced NAD, a coenzyme used to transfer hydrogen and electrons. Under anaerobic conditions the pyruvate is reduced to lactate in muscle (or ethanol and carbon dioxide in yeast). In the presence of oxygen the pyruvate enters the matrix of mitochondrion where it undergoes oxidative decarboxylation forming acetyl coenzyme A. This joins with a C4 intermediate and undergoes two further decarboxylation steps and oxidation forming ATP and reduced NAD and reduced FAD. The energy from the original glucose fuel is now stored in the electrons in the bonds of these reduced coenzymes.

Upon diffusion to the cristae, these electrons are passed along an electron transport chain in a series of redox reactions. As the electrons pass down, protein channels in the membrane become permeable to protons which then pass into the inter-membrane space, lowering its pH. This in turn opens a channel that allows the protons to flood back across the membrane generating an electrochemical gradient which activates ATPase in the stalk particles leading to the production of ATP. It is important to note that the respiration process also produces a lot of heat that is used to provide kinetic energy of processes such as osmosis and diffusion of molecules such as oxygen across exchange surfaces.

As previously mentioned the ATP is used to provide energy to a host of reactions in all organisms. In animals, hydrolysis of ATP provides energy for the detachment and formation of actomyosin cross bridges during muscle contraction. The ratchet process allows actin filaments to be drawn into myosin reducing the length of the sarcomere. In this way an animal, such as an antelope may run and avoid predation by cheetahs. Transfer of energy from ATP also plays a role in the transfer if nervous impulses along neurones to the muscles. ATP supplies energy for the pumping of three sodium ions out, and two potassium ions into the axon of a nerve against a concentration gradient. This resting potential of -70mV is then maintained by reduction of the membrane's permeability to sodium ions. Once an action potential arrives at a synapse or neuromuscular junction, ATP again provides the energy to move and fuse vesicles containing the neurotransmitter, acetylcholine which the pre-synaptic membrane.

Also in animals, kidneys use ATP for the active transport of sodium chloride out of the ascending limb of the loop of Henle in order to lower water potential in the surrounding tissues. This generates a water potential gradient which causes the reabsorption of water through the permeable descending limb leading to the production of more concentrated urine.

Plants require the translocation of glucose (as sucrose) from source cells to sinks (roots, fruits and shoots) to provide an energy source for non-photosynthetic tissues. This is achieved through active transport of sucrose (using energy from ATP) into the phloem which lowers water potential. This causes water to enter by osmosis generating a hydrostatic pressure which forces the sugar solution up and down the phloem towards the sink regions. In order to provide support, plants need a flow of water to enter the roots from the soil. This is achieved again by active transport of mineral ions such as potassium and nitrate from the soil, against a concentration gradient, using energy supplied by ATP. The lower water potential in the root hair cells now draws in water which moves towards the endodermis through the apoplast (gaps in the cell walls) and symplast (through cell cytoplasm) pathways.

In summary, this essay has shown how energy in light is transferred firstly to glucose, released as heat during respiration and stored as ATP, and how this molecule's hydrolysis releases energy that can be used by plants and animals for many important and diverse life-processes.

ESSAY 07: THE STRUCTURE AND FUNCTION RELATIONHIPS OF PROTEINS

Proteins are polymers of amino acids joined by strong peptide bonds. The combination of any of the twenty plus amino acids in any length and sequence allows an almost infinite number of possible structures and functions. This essay will detail how the variation in structure of the protein is related to specific functions.

The sequence of amino acids in the polypeptide chain is termed the primary structure. The primary structure is unique to a given protein. The primary structure can fold regularly to form either an α-helix or β-pleated sheet. The secondary structure is held together by hydrogen bonds between adjacent peptide bonds. The primary structure can further fold in an irregular but not random manner to form an overall three dimensional shape that more specifically determines the biological functions of the individual protein. This 3D structure is held together by bonds formed between the R-groups of amino acids. The bonds include hydrogen, ionic (between $R\text{-}COO^-$ and $^+H_3N\text{-}R$) or disulphide bridges. These bonds give a greater strength to the molecule allowing it to withstand some variations in temperature or pH.

Some proteins adopt a structural role. For example, keratin, a protein in skin, is formed from coils that twist together to form rope-like structures that are both flexible and strong. This strength is utilised in animals as claws or horns for predation or protection, or hair as camouflage or insulation. Collagen, another important structural protein that comprises connective tissue in animals, is composed of coils that are more tightly bound giving a more rigid structure.

For movement, animals use muscle contraction. Muscle fibres are composed of two protein filaments, myosin (a thicker filament) and actin (a thinner one). Actomyosin cross-bridges can form between the two which move relative to one another on hydrolysis of ATP drawing actin into myosin. This sliding filament theory shows how a sarcomere contracts. This contraction is used in a variety of applications including constriction or dilation of blood vessel to modify blood flow through tissues, pupil diameter to control light entry into eyes or the generation of a force at a joint to move a hand away from a hot object.

Some proteins adopt a transport role. Channel proteins in cell membranes offer a hydrophilic passage through the hydrophobic lipid bilayer. They have a specific three dimensional shape that is complementary to the given species they transport. For example, sodium gated channels in membranes of sensory neurones allow the passage of sodium into the axon during the generation of an action potential. Similar transport proteins are carrier proteins that can change shape on binding of their transporter molecule, e.g. glucose channel in liver cells to allow glucose to pass through the membrane in preparation for the process of glycogenesis.

Proteins form a key role in the infectivity of pathogens and the immunity of the host. Proteins on the surface of pathogenic bacteria act as antigens which identify a cell as non-host. Some of these antigens can break away and act as toxins. For example, the bacteria *Vibrium cholerae* releases a protein toxin that opens chloride ion channels in the large intestine causing loss of chloride from epithelial cells, and loss of large volumes of water as diarrhoea and chronic dehydration. Variation in the antigenic structure brought about by mutation of the pathogen's DNA can increase the infectivity of the pathogen as the host has no memory cells or antibodies to bind to and inactivate the antigen. Phagocytosis of pathogens eventually leads to activation of B-cells which divide by mitosis forming clones that differentiate to form plasma cells. These cells release antibodies that are globular proteins which have variable regions that have a complementary shape to a specific antigen, allowing it to agglutinate many pathogenic particles.

A key role for proteins is to act as enzymes; biological catalysts that lower activation energy of specific reactions, allowing them to take place under controlled conditions at body temperature. They have an active site that has a specific three-dimensional shape that is complementary shape to a given substrate. This provides specificity to reactions. On binding, the enzyme and substrate form an enzyme-substrate complex which places strain on the bonds allowing them to break more easily. For example, the enzyme sucrase has an active site that is complementary to the disaccharide sucrose. Lactose, another disaccharide that has a similar but subtly different shape to sucrose, will not fit into this site, and is therefore not hydrolysed by the enzyme. DNA polymerase condenses adjacent DNA-nucleotides together during the formation of the phosphate-sugar backbone of DNA during semi-conservative replication. Despite being similar in structure, RNA-nucleotides require RNA-polymerase to join them during transcription. These reactions highlight the high degree of specificity elicited by the flexible nature of the primary and tertiary structures of proteins.

Chemical coordination in animals is largely brought about using protein hormones. These hormones have a tertiary structure that is complementary to that of a receptor molecule (often another protein or glycoprotein) positioned on the cell-surface membrane of the target cell. Examples are insulin, a protein released by β-cells of the islets of Langerhan in the pancreas during conditions of high blood sugar concentrations. The insulin travels in the blood to hepatocytes in the liver and binds to a specific membrane receptor that causes activation of phosphorylase enzyme that condense glucose into glycogen in the process of glycogenesis. Glucagon is released from α-cells in the pancreas and stimulates the hydrolysis of glycogen into glucose when blood sugar is low. Other examples of endocrine hormones include follicle stimulating hormone that matures the ova in a follicle during the follicular phase of the menstrual cycle, and luteinising hormone, that causes rupture of the follicle and the release of the ova, once it has matured.

ESSAY 08: TRANSFERS ACROSS ECOSYSTEMS

An ecosystem comprises all the interactions between all the biotic (living) and abiotic (non-living) features in a given area at a given time. When these features interact, chemical elements, materials and energy are transferred and flow through the various components. This essay will describe these transfers with an emphasis on compounds of carbon, nitrogen, pesticides, water and energy.

Energy transfer through ecosystems takes place primarily by photosynthesis and respiration. Light energy is absorbed by chlorophyll in palisade cells of green plants. The energy is used to absorb electrons to higher energy levels. Once the electrons are passed down an electron transfer chain in a series of redox reactions, the energy released is used to activate the enzyme ATPase resulting in the production of ATP. Reduced NADP is also formed, in the light dependent reaction and these two products are then used to reduce glycerate-3-phosphate to triose phosphate in the Calvin cycle. The carbohydrate formed can then be used to synthesise glucose, lipids, starch, cellulose and other useful molecules which make up parts of the productivity of energy for the ecosystem. Thus the plants act as producers through transduction of the energy in sunlight and making it available in a chemical form.

The chemical potential energy in the form of the carbon containing compounds of the producers is then available for consumption by primary consumers, such as chickens, sheep and horses. These animals then eat the plants and digest some of the food molecules which they absorb and assimilate and use for growth, repair and respiration. The remaining biomass they cannot digest due to a lack of specific enzymes is egested and is made available for respiration by decomposer bacteria and fungi which decompose the faecal material by saprobiotic nutrition.

The carbohydrates absorbed by the animal are respired aerobically in the cells of the animal to release energy in the form of heat and ATP. Glucose enters the cells by facilitated diffusion and undergoes glycolysis in the cytoplasm. This involves the phosphorylation, and subsequent oxidation of the molecule to form pyruvate, and a net gain of two molecules of ATP. The pyruvate then diffuses into the mitochondrion where it undergoes decarboxylation in the link reaction forming acetyl co-enzyme A, a two-carbon molecule that combines with a C4 to form a C6, that is decarboxylated and oxidised systematically to release CO_2, some ATP and reduced co-enzymes such as reduced NAD and reduced FAD. These coenzymes release their energy during oxidative phosphorylation in the electron transport chain where it is used to form large amounts of ATP (38 molecules per respired glucose).

This energy is used by the animal for processes such as active transport of sodium and potassium ions into and out of the axon of a nerve cell in the generation of a resting potential, or in the detachment and reformation of actomyosin cross bridges as part of muscle contraction for movement. In this way, some more of the energy consumed by the animal is lost as to the environment as heat and so less is available to secondary consumers such as foxes when they consume the chickens. It is these losses as the food chain is transversed that create the pyramids of biomass and energy at each trophic level. Less and less energy is available to the next trophic level as more and more is lost through movement, heat and excretion.

One key chemical element that is recycled and transferred around ecosystems is nitrogen. All organisms have DNA as their genetic code and DNA is composed of nucleotides such as adenine and thymine that have nitrogenous bases. The DNA codes for proteins which in turn contain nitrogen in the amino acid monomers of which they are composed. Atmospheric nitrogen, an unreactive element, is fixed by nitrogen-fixing bacteria such as Rhizobium in the root nodules of leguminous plants to form ammonium ions that are released into the soil. Nitrifying bacteria then oxidise the ammonium to nitrite and then nitrate, which can either be denitrified to nitrogen or absorbed by plants through the root hair cells by active transport. The plant can then assimilate the nitrogen into its biomass, and on death, decomposer fungi can hydrolyse the proteins into amino acids and de-aminate them to ammonium which is release back in the soil for nitrification. Since the plants biomass can also be consumed by the consumers as previously discussed, the nitrogen can be cycled and recycled around the ecosystem being made available for assimilation into biologically important molecules as it is transferred.

Another important material that is transferred is water. Water evaporates from the sea and condenses as a cloud. The water then falls back to the earth as rain. Plants can absorb the water from the soil by actively transporting mineral ions into their root hair cells to lower water potential, allowing water to enter by osmosis. The water is forced up the xylem through the generation of a root pressure by the pumping of ions into the xylem to lower water potential. Evaporation of water through the gas exchange surface, the stomata on the underside of the leaf, draws water up the xylem by cohesion-tension creating a transpiration stream that returns the water to the atmosphere.

Animals also use the water they drink to transport hydrophilic substances such as glucose through their blood. The water is lost back to the environment in three ways, i) through loss as sweat when used to regulate body temperature through the evaporation from the skin, ii) excretion of water from the bladder as a concentrated urine, that was produced by the kidneys to remove the metabolic waste product, urea, or iii) loss through the exchange surface of the lungs when exhaling.

Finally, other materials can be transferred through ecosystems. These include genetic material (when the pollen grains of plants fertilise or the eggs and sperm fuse during sexual reproduction) or man-made substances such as pesticides that can undergo bioaccumulation in organisms as they move up the food chain due to their incorporation into fatty tissues.

This essay has highlighted the transfers of a diverse range of materials and energy through the biotic and abiotic components of an ecosystem.

ESSAY 09: THE SAME PARENTS MAY PRODUCE OFFSPRING THAT DIFFER FROM EACH OTHER. DISCUSS HOW THIS IS BROUGHT ABOUT

Different offspring from the same parents inherit the same genetic information when the haploid gametes produced by the parents in meiosis fuse to form the zygote which then divides to form the embryo. Despite this, they may have different appearances or phenotypes as they are known. This essay will explore some of the reasons behind these differences.

The characteristics of an organism are encoded within its genes. Genes are sequences of bases on DNA which code for the sequence of amino acids in a polypeptide chain. Since proteins, as enzymes and gene expression factors, determine the structure and functions of cells, they determine the development of an organism. While organisms of the same species carry the same genes at given loci, the structures of the genes vary. These alternate forms of genes or alleles can give rise to the intraspecific variations seen within populations of the same species.

Variation in alleles can be due to factors such as mutation or through crossing over or independent segregation in meiosis. Mutations, such as substitution mutations, alter the base sequence of DNA, which in turn alters the complementary mRNA formed at transcription and so the sequence of amino acids in the protein that was coded for. They may occur randomly during the semi-conservative replication of DNA during later interphase of mitosis, or as a result of exposure to an environmental mutagen. X-rays and many estrogenic chemicals found in food packaging, for example can cause subtle alterations in the base sequence. If, for example the mutated base sequence now codes for a non-functional form of an enzyme that causes the darkening of a yellow pigment to brown in the coats of a Labrador, then one offspring of two chocolate Labradors may appear pale yellow due to the presence of the mutation, whereas another puppy may be darker due to normal amounts of pigment being deposited in the fur.

Mutations can be relatively rare, but meiosis is adapted to bring variation into a sexually reproducing population. Meiosis is the process of cell division that halves the chromosome number to produce haploid cells that are genetically different. This is an important process as it not only introduces genetic variations into a population, but also allows the restoration of the diploid number of chromosomes on fertilisation. During the first division of meiosis, homologous chromosomes line up with their partners and crossing over may occur. The homologous chromosomes join at points called chiasmata and sections of the chromatids are exchanged resulting in new recombinations of maternal and paternal alleles. Each of the four new daughter cells formed will carry one copy of each chromosome. Before these chromosomes are separated into the cells, they align randomly along the equator of the cell. One of each of the four versions of the twenty three homologous pairs (in the case of humans) is randomly and independently segregated into a daughter cell, resulting in new combinations of maternal and paternal chromosomes.

In this way, each gamete formed by both parent is genetically unique, and since the process of sexual reproduction is a random event in that any sperm may fertilise the particular ovum released during that particular menstrual cycle, then no two offspring from the same parents can carry exactly the same alleles. Since it is these the combined effects of alleles and the environment which ultimately determine the nature and appearance of the offspring, no two offspring will appear identical.

The genotype of an organism is its genetic constitution, in other words the alleles that make up each gene. For example, the gene for eye colour may have two alleles B (brown) being dominant to b (blue). Two heterozygous parents each carrying Bb will each form gametes B and b, which could combine by random fusion during sexual reproduction forming a variety of possible combinations, e.g. BB or Bb which would give a brown eyed offspring, of bb which would give blue eyed. Since every gene has two alleles, there are a multitude of possible combinations of subtle differences in phenotype, each of which could give rise to slightly different offspring. Such examples of discontinuous variation give rise to differences in the offspring of a set of parents, but also the multitude of other polygenetic inherited characteristics combine to give wide variations in the siblings produced. For example, one sibling may have darker hair than another, be taller and have blue eyes compared to a shorter, blonder, brown eyed sibling.

An organism inherits its alleles from its parents, but offspring from the same parents are rarely similar in appearance. Even identical twins with the same genotype, can vary due to subtle differences in environmental factors that influence them in different ways. For example, each twin may be influenced by peer pressure to eat different foods and or take part in different sports. Thus one twin, the one who took part in sports may appear leaner and have a more defined musculature than the less athletic one. The effects of childhood illness or conditions such as acne may also create differences in the appearance of the siblings later in life. One sibling who may have developed severe acne may be more facially scarred that one who didn't.

Environmental influences are present in all species. One key factor in plants for example is the availability of key nutrients or energy. Two dandelion plants from the same parents may differ in appearance if one has been grown in a shaded and dry field poor in magnesium. This plant would appear more yellow compared to another grown in magnesium rich soil.

While it is difficult to ascribe exact causes to subtle intraspecific variations, even those obvious in siblings of the same parents, some of the genetic and environmental reasons behind those differences are understood. The variation it creates is of key importance to the population as it creates a large gene pool that has a greater ability to adapt and survive under more adverse or hostile conditions. The genetic and environmental causes of variation described here contribute to this diversity.

ESSAY 10: HOW CARBON DIOXIDE AFFECCTS ORGANISMS AND ECOSYSTEMS

An ecosystem comprises all the interactions between the biotic (living) and abiotic (non-living) features in a given area at a given time. One key molecule that is of fundamental importance to these interactions is carbon dioxide, as it transfers carbon atoms between organisms and organisms with their environment. This essay will explore some of the important roles of CO_2 in a variety of organisms such as plants and animals.

Today's atmosphere contains low levels of CO_2, a gas that is a limiting factor for productivity in an ecosystem. Plants can absorb it through their gas exchange surface, the stomata, on the underside of the leaves. If diffuses through the air spaces and diffuses into the stroma of chloroplasts inside palisade cells. There it is combined with RuBP and is reduced by the products of the light dependent reaction of photosynthesis (reduced NAD and ATP) to triose phosphate. This, simple monosaccharide is then combined into larger molecules such as glucose, and ultimately the polysaccharides starch and cellulose. In this way, the carbon dioxide acted as a source of carbon atoms which were incorporated into the biomass of the plants, and therefore the available biomass of an ecosystem. It follows that the higher the CO_2 levels in the atmosphere, the higher the productivity, but other limiting factors such as temperature, pollution and availability of water and nutrients in the soil will also play a role.

This biomass of the producers may then be consumed by herbivores such as sheep to provide energy and the building blocks for growth and repair. The food, e.g. starch formed by the plants, is digested by amylase to maltose and then by maltase into alpha-glucose. The glucose can then enter cells where it undergoes aerobic respiration, a process that provides energy in the form of ATP but also releases the CO_2 back out into the atmosphere. The glucose is oxidised to pyruvate, which is then systematically decarboxylated in the link and Krebs cycle in the matrix of the mitochondria. Decarboxylation releases CO_2 and reduced coenzymes such as reduced NAD and reduced FAD from which ATP will be produced by oxidative phosphorylation in the cristae.

The carbon dioxide is released as a waste gas and accumulates in the tissue fluid of the respiring cells. Here, it plays a key role in oxygen transport and delivery to respiring cells. Oxygen is bound to haemoglobin in the form of oxyhaemoglobin. When the partial pressure of oxygen is low, for example when CO_2 is formed by respiring muscle cells, then the oxygen is unloaded from the haemoglobin in the red blood cells and is made available for respiration. The carbon dioxide then replaces oxygen on the haemoglobin and can be transported to the lungs where it is returned to the atmosphere when expiration takes place.

The CO_2 also has some important physiological roles. An increased rate of respiration, for example as a person runs, produces more waste CO_2 at a time when the oxygen demand is high. The CO_2 dissolves in the blood plasma releasing hydrogen ions which lower pH. This reduced pH causes a shift in the oxygen dissociation curve to the right further reducing the affinity of haemoglobin for oxygen. At this lower partial pressure, and with a shifted curve, even greater amounts of oxygen are unloaded and made available for respiration.

In order to satisfy the need to inspire more oxygen and expire more carbon dioxide to accommodate this increased rate of respiration, the CO_2 also acts on chemoreceptors in the walls of the carotid arteries and aorta. The reduced pH caused by the dissociation of CO_2 in the blood plasma activates these chemoreceptors which send an increased frequency of impulses to the cardio-acceleratory centre in the medulla of the brain. This in turn sends an increased frequency of sympathetic nervous impulses to the sinoatrial node, the pacemaker in the wall of the right atrium, causing it to send an increased frequency of waves of excitation, increasing the heart rate. This increased heart rate increases the cardiac output resulting in a faster delivery of blood to the gas exchange surfaces, the alveoli in the lungs. Thus, more oxygen can be transported around the body, and more CO_2 returned to the atmosphere.

Since all living organisms respire, the carbon dioxide removed by plants for photosynthesis is constantly replaced. This constant recycling of carbon is crucial to the existence of all life on this planet, as changing carbon dioxide concentration could have disastrous consequences for all life. Each organism is adapted by natural selection to exist optimally within its environment to increase its chances of survival. Human activities such as deforestation and the burning of fossil fuels to provide energy have resulted in an increase in atmospheric carbon dioxide concentrations. The C=O bonds of the gas can trap infra-red radiation and prevent it from being radiated back out into space. This extra trapped kinetic energy causes a warming effect referred to as global warming. The global consequences of this phenomenon are wide and diverse in that polar ice caps are melting, changing the environment for organisms that are adapted for arctic conditions. The increased sea levels may cause flooding of low-lying coastal land, increasing the salination of soil, but decreasing the concentration of salt in sea. These changes will act as selection pressures on organisms, forcing the process of natural selection. Those members of a given species that are best adapted to survive the changes are more likely to survive and pass on their beneficial alleles to their offspring. In this way, the allele frequencies may change, ultimately altering the phenotypes. For example, salination of soil causes by coastal flooding would favour xerophytically adapted plants, as the reduced water potential in the soil would make it hard for the plant to take up enough water for its needs. Xerophytic adaptions such as sunken stomata and rolled leaves would help reduce water loss by evaporation, reducing transpiration rates.

Such huge changes in the environment would destabilise the complex food webs and reduce diversity. While carbon dioxide levels are only one factor in environmental change, the molecules' key importance to life makes it essential that its levels are closely monitored and action taken to minimise the various impacts of its change.

ESSAY 11: DESCRIBE HOW THE SHAPES OF CELLS IS RELATED TO THEIR FUNCTIONS

The cell is the simplest living unit of which all tissues, organs and organisms are built up. In multicellular organisms these cells differentiate and become specialised to perform a given function. These specialisations then impact on the shapes and structures of the cells. This essay will describe how the shapes of some examples of animal and plant cells relate to the cell's function.

Species in the kingdom *Plantae*, are anchored in the soil by their roots. The functions of these roots include the absorption of water and mineral ions from the soil which they deliver to the xylem for transport up and around the plant. The roots have an outer layer of cells called root hair cells that are adapted for this purpose. The cells have a long thin extension of the cell surface membrane that extends into the soil. This dramatically increases the surface area of the membrane and hence the number of channel proteins. Minerals such as nitrate and potassium ions are transported across this membrane by active transport using energy supplied by ATP. The ions pass through a specific hydrophilic channel protein against a concentration gradient. A higher surface area of membrane means a greater concentration of these channels and so a greater efficiency in the absorption from the soil. These ions then lower the water potential inside the root hair cell allowing water to enter by osmosis. Here again, the presence of a greater number of hydrophilic channels offer the small water molecules an easy passage through the membrane.

The water moves via the apoplast and symplast pathways to the endodermis, where it enters the xylem tissue, the vascular route by which water passes up the stem of the plant. The xylem tissue is composed of xylem vessels that are tube-shaped hollow cells with pits in the side. They are hollow to allow an unhindered passage of water up through the plant. The absence of organelles further facilitates the passage of water. The pits in the sides allow lateral passage of ions from the xylem out into the surrounding tissues to lower water potential, allowing water to pass out and be used for support, and, amongst other things, photosynthesis.

Plants are a kingdom of species that are autotrophic. They derive their energy through photosynthesis by absorbing specific wavelengths of sunlight and converting it into chemical potential energy, driving the combination of carbon dioxide and water to form glucose and oxygen. The palisade cells are situated mainly on the upper surface of the leaf and have adaptations for the absorption of specific wavelengths of red and blue light. The palisade cells have a block-like shape that allows them to stack together with little gaps between them like bricks in a wall. This presents a high surface area for light to strike which increases the efficiency of the process. Each palisade cell has a large number of chloroplasts which contain the green pigment chlorophyll which absorbs the energy and uses it to excite electrons in the light-dependant reaction of photosynthesis. When their energy is released, in the electron transport chain, ATP and reduced NADP are formed which are used to reduce glycerate-3-phosphate to triose phosphate and ultimately glucose.

Animals are a kingdom of species that are heterotrophic. They derive their energy by consuming, digesting and absorbing plant and animal matter which they use to provide nutrients such as carbohydrate and lipid for their growth and repair. The polysaccharide starch, formed from the glucose in plants, is consumed by herbivores and digested in the gut by amylase to maltose. This disaccharide is then further hydrolysed by maltase in the intestinal epithelium to glucose which is absorbed by the epithelial cells located there. These epithelial cells have a brush border composed of microvilli, close-packed folded extensions of the membrane that massively increase the surface area and the concentration of channels. The glucose is absorbed through a sodium-glucose co-transporter protein on the cell surface. The many mitochondria inside these cells provide ATP by respiration for the active transport of a potassium ion from the blood into the cell at the same time as transporting a sodium ion out. This lowers the concentration of sodium ions inside creating a gradient that draws in the sodium and the glucose through the co-transporter protein. Glucose channels on the basement membrane then allow the glucose to enter the blood by facilitated diffusion.

One of the roles of glucose in the animal is to supply a source of energy for aerobic respiration. This process requires a delivery of oxygen from the lungs to the respiring tissues. The oxygen is carried bound to haemoglobin inside red blood cells, small cells that have a biconcave shape that can flex easily and offer a high surface area of contact with the capillary walls for efficient gas exchange. This reduces the diffusion pathway of the oxygen and carbon dioxide increasing gas exchange rates. An absence of organelles also increases the room available for the haemoglobin, each molecule of which can load four oxygen molecules.

The respiration of this glucose provides energy in the form of ATP. This is used to power a multitude of process including the generation of a resting potential in a nerve cell. A nerve cell, or neurone, is adapted for the passage of electrical impulses from the central nervous system to remote effectors or from receptors. Thread-like extensions of the membranes or dendrites allow the synapsing of information with other neurones allowing the propagation of the action potentials to more effectors. A long thin myelinated axon allows a direct connection from the central nervous system, along which the waves of depolarisation can pass. The rate of conductance of these impulses is further increased by the presence of myelination which effectively insulates the membrane allowing impulses to pass only at the nodes of Ranvier. The cell body of sensory neurones is located off to the side of the axon so as not to interfere with the passage of the impulses.

ESSAY 12: LIPIDS IN HEALTH AND DISEASE

Lipids are molecules containing carbon, hydrogen, oxygen and sometimes phosphorous atoms which play important roles in health and disease. This essay will examine some of these functions and look at how they contribute to health and disease.

Triglycerides are lipids that are composed of a glycerol head group linked by an ester linkage to three fatty acid tails formed by condensation reactions. The fatty acid tails can be saturated, in that they contain only carbon to carbon single bonds, or be unsaturated with at least one double bond. The tails can be up to approximately seventeen carbon atoms long giving rise to the molecule's very hydrophobic (water hating) properties. This hydrophobic nature makes them insoluble and so good candidates for storage functions.

Lipids have a lower density than water which also makes them good thermal insulators. Many animals have a thin layer of saturated fats under the skin which helps to minimise heat loss through radiation. This means that they contribute to an animal's ability to maintain its body temperature by homeostasis. This is more pronounced in animals that are adapted to arctic conditions. Often these animals are much larger and have a thicker layer of fat beneath the skin. The increased size this gives lowers the surface area to volume ratio resulting in a lower effective surface from which heat would be lost. Coupled with more insulation, this means the animal would need a lower respiration rate in order to survive, thus helping to preserve fuel sources.

The dense number of carbon to carbon and carbon to hydrogen bonds in lipids makes these molecules energy rich and so they can act as useful fuels. A fuel is any substance that releases energy in a useful form when reacted with oxygen. Hydrolysis of triglycerides by lipase enzymes in adipose tissue releases fatty acids which can be converted to respiratory substrates such as glucose in the process of gluconeogenesis. In healthy individuals, carbohydrates are the usual energy source unless exercise reduces the blood glucose concentrations resulting in hypoglycaemia. In such situations, gluconeogenesis represents a mechanism by which new glucose can be synthesised to provide energy in the liver from glycerol. This is also useful in situations such as diabetes where a sufferer may become hypoglycaemic if they take too much insulin or do not replace glucose when exercising. Fatty acids can be converted to glucose enabling a diabetic to make more glucose available despite having limited glycogen stores.

The energy rich lipid molecules therefore represent a key component of any diet. They not only provide energy (about nine kCal/g) but can dissolve certain fat soluble vitamins which allow them to be absorbed and transported through the body. In this sense they are key to the health of an individual, but too much intake in the diet can lead to obesity which can have a profound impact on health. Obesity increases the risk of coronary heart disease and increase the risk of myocardial infarction though the formation atheroma. Atheroma is the formation of a fatty deposit on the inside wall of the arteries. In the coronary artery these can lead to a reduced blood supply to the heart resulting in the death of muscle cells through lack of oxygen, resulting in myocardial infarction. Restricted blood flow can also contribute to high blood pressure, the risk of stroke and other circulatory disorders. Obesity is also an important risk factor in the development of diabetes in later life. However, unsaturated fats such as those found in nuts and seeds can be a healthier alternative to saturated animal fats. Plants can grow from nuts and seeds and these contain the genetic information for the plants development. They are also a rich source of unsaturated fats which act as the energy source for the germinating seed.

Another type of lipid is a phospholipid. These molecules are similar to triglycerides but have one of the fatty acids substituted by a phosphate ion. This ion gives hydrophilic properties to the head, which combined with the hydrophobic tails gives these molecules the unique property of being able to align to form a phospholipid bilayer, the basis of the cell membrane. In the bilayer, the hydrophobic tails can align producing a structure with hydrophilic properties on either side which can interact with the aqueous environment inside and outside the cell. The molecules can move relative to each other, forming the fluid aspect to the fluid-mosaic model. The mosaic aspect is related to the embedding of other structures such as glycolipids. These are lipids with carbohydrate structures attached that can act as recognition sites for antigens on the surface of bacteria such as *Vibrio cholerae*. In this way they can contribute to the infectivity and pathogenicity of some viruses and bacteria in that they represent a means by which these cells or their toxins can enter the host cell to infect them and cause disease. In the case of Vibrio cholerae, binding of a toxin to glycolipids attached to chloride ion channels can cause cholera resulting in the severe life-threatening diarrhoea and dehydration.

Also embedded within the bilayer is another type of lipid, cholesterol. This ring-like lipid not only adds strength to the membrane but also acts as a precursor molecule to synthesise other related substances such as oestrogen and progesterone, sex hormones involved in control of the female menstrual cycle. Oestrogen is a steroid that stimulates the uterus lining to thicken, while a different steroid, progesterone, helps maintain the thickened lining. Oestrogen is also involved in a negative feedback loop with the protein hormone FSH which causes the follicles to mature the developing ovum. The ovum releases oestrogen which in turn reduces the release of FSH from the pituitary gland. This feedback is exploited in contraceptive pills where the elevated levels of oestrogen reduce the FSH to low levels preventing the maturation of the ovum.

Another important role for a lipid is in the acceleration of nerve impulse in sensory and motor neurones of animals. A lipid, myelin, wraps around the membrane of nerve cells forming an insulating sheath around the axon. Action potentials cannot form in these regions, and so impulse cannot travel along the axon at this point. Instead they jump across the *Nodes of Ranvier*, small gaps between the myelin sheaths by salutatory conduction, increasing the speed of conductance. In some diseases such as motor neurone disease, the sheath peels away resulting in a slower conductance of impulses along nerves.

This essay has identified the structures and functions of different kinds of lipids and emphasised their importance in normal healthy conditions and some disease states.

ESSAY 13: GENES AND DIVERSITY

Genes are sequences of bases on DNA that code for the amino acid's sequence on a polypeptide chain. As polypeptides control the nature and development of organisms, genes are responsible for the diversity of life on this planet. This essay will detail how genes and their alleles are responsible for introducing diversity.

DNA is a double-stranded polymer of two complementary polynucleotide strands joined through specific base pairing by hydrogen bonds. The sequences of bases on DNA are arranged in sections called genes that occur at the same positions, or loci, along a chromosome. The bases are arranged in triplets, each triplet codon coding for a specific amino acid in a polypeptide chain. Not all of the DNA in the gene codes for the amino acids. Also included are non-coding regions called introns which are removed during the post transcriptional modification of the pre-mRNA to form the mRNA from which the protein is translated.

While each member of the same species has the same genes at a given loci, there are different versions of the genes called alleles. Differences in the allele structures arise from mutations or are introduced by meiosis. Mutations are alterations in the base structure of the gene that result from either copying errors during semi-conservative replication of DNA or by the influence of mutagens such as x-rays. The alterations may influence the primary (and so tertiary structure) of the protein coded for. In the case of bacteria, for example, this may now incur resistance to an antibiotic and so provide a benefit to the individual cell. This has introduced diversity into an otherwise genetically uniform population of bacteria since their normal mode of replication is asexual in nature. In sexually reproducing organisms the process of meiosis introduces variation through the processes of crossing over or independent segregation. Homologous chromosomes align in the first meiotic division and form links called chiasmata. Sections of the chromatids are then exchanged producing four genetically distinct versions each with a new recombination of maternal and paternal alleles. The random alignment of these chromosomes prior to separation into the four daughter cells further shuffles the combinations by independent segregation forming new combinations of maternal and paternal alleles and their genes.

Random fusion of these gametes on fertilisation further contributes to the diversity of the population of the species. The diversity is seen in the range of phenotypes and is referred to as intra-specific variation. This accounts for the subtly different phenotypes observed in a population. For example some humans have blue and some brown, some of blood group A and some of group O.

These variations in phenotype contribute to the differential survival of some members of the species when they are exposed to a selection pressure. For example, within a population of antelope there may be a range of alleles which cause continuous variation in leg length that is further affected by polygenic and environmental factors influencing the phenotype. Some of these alleles may confer a benefit to the organism which has them, so the longer legged antelope may be able to effectively outrun a natural predator such as a cheetah that can run very quickly over shorter distances. So the long legged antelopes are more likely to survive to maturity and pass on these alleles to the next generation offspring, increasing that allele frequency.

Through this process of natural selection, the genes and their alleles are helping the populations to adapt to their environment, a process that can reduce diversity in the gene pool as those less adapted members die out. Adaptations may be anatomical, physiological or behavioural. Anatomical adaptions include xerophytic adaptations of plants that become adapted to hot and dry conditions to limit water loss. Features such as sunken stomata, a low surface are to volume ratio and rolled leaves are more likely to be selected for. Physiological adaptations may include subtle shifts in the oxygen dissociation curve of haemoglobin as evidence by deer mice from high altitudes have a dissociation curve that lies to the left of that of deer mice from valley regions. This means it the haemoglobin has a higher affinity for oxygen so at any given partial pressure of oxygen there is greater loading and oxygen saturation, to make oxygen available for respiration. Behavioural adaptions include diversity of mating rituals that ensure only those receptive females of the same species are mated with the male when the chances of fertilisation are maximised.

Such adaptations are of vital importance when populations become isolated either geographically (by mountain ranges or rivers) or behaviourally (by variations in courtship ritual etc) and can contribute to speciation over many thousands of years. The isolated populations become exposed to a variety of selection pressures including predation, disease, and inter-specific competition which forces natural selection and adaptations. The alteration in allele frequencies this causes can alter the gene and chromosome structure meaning the gametes formed are no longer compatible and fertile offspring cannot be produced on interbreeding.

Differences in gene structure introduced by speciation can be observed by comparing the DNA sequences from different species by DNA hybridisation. Single stranded DNA from the two species being compared are mixed and hydrogen bonds are allowed to form between the two polynucleotide strands. The temperature can then be increased and the point recorded at which the strands separate. The more closely related a species, the more complementary base pairings take place between A to T and C to G and so more energy is needed to separate the strands. This is one way scientists are able to classify the relationships between species in order to calculate species diversity index within an environment to facilitate studies of the interactions between organisms, for example during succession. Hybridisation data can also be used to construct phylogenetic trees which describe the familial relationships to a common ancestor.

This essay has shown how variations in the base sequence of DNA can lead to changes alleles and the proteins expressed from them. Such alterations introduce diversity, not only into members of a given species but can contribute to that population's long term survival

ESSAY 14: THE PHYSIOLOGICAL IMPACT OF LIFESTYLE ON HEALTH

Health can be defined as the optimal functioning of body and mind. The way in which we live our lives can have a profound effect on the physiological processes which take place in our bodies. This essay will describe the connections between our lifestyle choices and health.

To fuel our life processes we eat food. Food contains the necessary building blocks (such as proteins, carbohydrates and fats) which supply energy, atoms and molecules for growth and repair and physiological processes. Small amounts of vitamins and minerals ions such as calcium and iron also contribute to the optimal functioning of our bodies.

Whilst a certain quantity of food is essential for life, those who overeat can develop serious health risks. Overeating foods such as saturated fats can lead to obesity over time. The heavier the person, the more the ventricles of the heart have to contract to deliver blood to the whole of the body. This, together with the formation of fatty deposits on the inside of arterial walls, called atheroma can lead to high blood pressure and reduced blood flow to tissues and increase the risk of coronary heart disease. In extreme cases, for example the coronary artery may become blocked reducing the supply of oxygen to the heart muscle causing it to die. The resulting myocardial infarction is life threatening. Consumption of too much processed foods with a high sugar content can also lead to obesity, and an increased risk of diabetes. Diabetes is a condition in which the body's regulation of blood glucose is impaired. In this condition, the glycoprotein receptors on the cell surface membrane become unresponsive to the protein hormone insulin, released from the pancreas in response to high blood glucose levels. This prevents the elevated blood glucose concentrations from decreasing to normal amounts which lowers blood water potential. This can lead to (i) increased tissue dehydration which impairs normal cellular functions, (ii) an increase in blood pressure which increases the risk of aneurysm (iii) a decreased release of ADH from the pituitary further causing reduce water uptake from the collecting ducts of the kidneys, dehydration and increased frequency of urination.

Eating foods low in minerals such as iron and calcium can also have a negative impact on health. Iron is a key component of the protein haemoglobin which transports oxygen from the lungs to the respiring tissues and removes the by-product of aerobic respiration, carbon dioxide. A lack of iron results in fewer red blood cells and so results in reduced respiration. One key impact of this is the reduction in cellular levels of ATP. Calcium ions contribute to the hydrolysis of ATP by the enzyme ATPase which provides energy for the detachment and formation of actomyosin cross-bridges resulting in the contraction of muscles. Less ATP hydrolysis would result in a reduced force of contraction and reduce the ability of the person to exercise. In turn less exercise in associated with an increased risk of coronary heart disease and high blood pressure. This negative cycle on health can therefore be avoided by taking a varied and balanced diet with lots of exercise.

Where we choose to live can also have a physiological impact on our bodies. Living at altitude where the partial pressure of oxygen is low will lead to adaptations where the oxygen-haemoglobin dissociation curve shifts up and to the left. This increases the affinity of haemoglobin for oxygen making it easier to load. The cooler climate will result in less activation of thermoreceptors in the skin, and an increased activity of the heat gain centre in the hypothalamus. This will send an increased frequency of impulses to effectors such as core muscles leading to shivering, or cause contraction of erector muscles beneath the skin leading to hairs standing up.

Living in cities with a high degree of air pollution can affect lung function and cause diseases such as asthma and pulmonary fibrosis. In asthma the airways become inflamed and irritated in response to exposure to pollens or dust. In response, large amounts of mucus are formed with constrict the airways causing breathing difficulties. Exposure to dust and pollutants can also result in the build up of scar tissue called fibrosis that decreases the elasticity of the lungs meaning a reduction in the pulmonary ventilation rate.

Choosing to smoke cigarettes exposes the lungs to carbon monoxide but also to tar and its mutagenic or carcinogenic contents. Carbon monoxide binds irreversibly to haemoglobin resulting in less oxygen transport and efficient gas exchange. This is particularly relevant to pregnant women who have to exchange gases at the placenta to the foetus. Reduced oxygen to the foetus results in less oxygen and respiration in the baby and therefore reduces its growth potential. Mutagenic agents in tar can alter the base sequence of DNA in the lung cells. This can lead to an alteration in the structure of the mRNA formed on transcription and the polypeptide produced. If this protein is an enzyme then it may not fold and adopt the correct tertiary structure of the active site and so result in the formation of a non-functional enzyme. Activation of the proto-oncogene can also permanently switch on mitosis of the lung cells leading to the formation of tumours.

Even our level of personal hygiene can impact on health. Failure to wash hands after defecation or drinking water contaminated with faecal matter can result in exposure to pathogens such as *Vibrio cholerae* which cause life-threatening dehydration. The bacteria release a part of its antigen, a toxin into the intestinal epithelial which increases the cells permeability to chloride ions. The loss of chloride into the lumen lowers water potential causing loss of body water through severe diarrhoea.

Our lifestyles affect how our bodies interact with our environment. This essay has established a link between the lives we choose to lead and the impact it has on our health and physiology.

ESSAY 15: THE IMPACT OF HUMAN ACTIVITIES ON THE DIVERSITY OF PLANTS AND ANIMALS

Diversity of life on this planet is a measure of not only the number of different species but the abundance of each species within a community. Human activities such as the burning of fossil fuels, farming and deforestation can have a dramatic impact on diversity. This essay will draw some connections between these activities and changing diversity.

One of the biggest global challenges at the moment is reducing the impact of global warming and dimming on the ecosystem. An ecosystem comprises all the interactions between the biotic (living) and abiotic (non-living) factors. Of fundamental importance is the increase in atmospheric dust and carbon dioxide concentration resulting from the burning of fossil fuels which are used by humans to provide energy for their daily lives. The dust and particles of pollution are leading to global dimming, a reduction in the amounts of light striking the Earth's surface. Light energy is the source of energy for photosynthetic producers such as plants and protoctists such as seaweeds. These organisms have pigments such as chlorophyll which absorbs specific wavelengths of light energy, and transferring it through photosynthesis into chemical energy in the form of glucose and ATP. A light dependent reaction excites electrons and passes them along an electron transfer chain which releases energy that is used to form ATP and reduced NADP. These molecule are then used to reduce carbon dioxide to triose phosphate and then glucose in the Calvin cycle of the light independent reaction in the stroma of the chloroplasts. The glucose is then converted to a host of useful materials such as starch and cellulose which comprise the biomass of the plants themselves.

Reduced photosynthesis will challenge those plants that are best adapted for bright conditions and favour more shade-adapted species. Unless natural selections can keep pace with change, this could lead to many plant species dying out, reducing diversity of producers. But these plants act not only as food for consumers but offer shelter and habitat for smaller animals, birds and insects. They support a complex network of ecological connections known as a food web, and loss of any species here can mean the extinction of those organisms that feed on them, or rely on them for protection. For example, a loss of a plant such as bamboo in China may not only reduce net productivity and oxygen release as a whole, but further challenge the existence of the Giant Panda which feeds almost exclusively on it. In this way whole food chains may become unstable leading to a dramatic decrease in species diversity or abundance. In some situations this may lead to genetic bottlenecks that will reduce the gene pools of those species that can survive better, further reducing their ability to adapt to future change.

The increased carbon dioxide released as a result of the combustion of fossil fuels absorbs some of the infra-red radiation that would normally be radiated out into space, leading to global warming. This has huge consequences for a wide variety of plants and animals. Increased temperatures are leading to the melting of polar ice caps.   This reduces the environment available for animals adapted to cold conditions such as polar bears. Anatomical adaptations, such as thick white fur and large amounts of subcutaneous fat acting as thermal insulation will no longer be of benefit. This could lead either to the deaths of larger predators such as these, or be a catalyst for phenotypic change through natural selection.   The polar bear population shows intra-specific variations caused by crossing over and independent segregation in meiosis. Some of these individuals may have alleles that make them smaller and darker than others which may now be a benefit. These individuals are more likely to survive to maturity and pass on these beneficial alleles to their offspring, so increasing its frequency in the population. In this way the phenotype will change, and over long periods of time lead to further speciation and an increase in diversity of isolated populations. However the pace of environmental change is faster than many species can adapt and so, on balance, the diversity index of environments will likely fall.

Not only natural selection, but artificial selection also acts to reduce diversity. Farmers may choose to propagate high-yielding crops by breeding together the best strains, or even killing off poorer varieties. This leads to a dramatic reduction in alleles creating a bottleneck that reduces the ability of the surviving members to adapt to change. In many cases this even makes them prone to a higher incidence of genetic disorders. This is also seen in cattle, for example, where dairy farmers may choose to only stock and breed specific breeds that are better milk producers. While such practices may increase the hardiness of some breeds or benefit humans in food production, it can cause suffering and health problems and reduce life expectancy in the animals themselves.

There are, however some practices that help to locally increase the diversity of communities. Conservation of wildlife sanctuaries or the creation of ideal conditions for the repopulation of specific organisms such as field orchids, etc can enhance the local diversity through the attraction of insects and birds. In Africa, the conservation of the elephant population that was almost hunted into extinction will help to maintain the variety of the local habitat.

While farming and deforestation reduces diversity, allowing areas to recover and a natural succession to take place will enhance it. Succession is the process whereby pioneer species such as lichens will colonise a hostile area and make the conditions more favourable for longer lived organisms such as mosses and grasses. In turn this attracts insects, and so birds and larger mammals, increasing the complexity and stability of the food webs. This leads to a large increase in the index of diversity until it reaches a climax community. By leaving former farmland to mature in this way, the process of succession leads to a partial recovery of the environment from the harmful activities of man.

ESSAY 16: RECEPTORS AND THEIR ROLE IN COORDINATION

Receptors are structures that detect specific stimuli and transduce their energy into nerve impulse as a form the body can interpret allowing the coordination of an appropriate response. Receptors can detect external stimuli including light, temperature, chemicals and pressure; internal stimuli can be electrical, chemical, thermal, pressure or osmotic. This essay will discuss the variety of receptors and outline how each plays its role in coordination.

Simple organisms such as woodlice are prone to dehydration. They are able to detect threatening decreases in a non-directional stimulus such as humidity via receptors. This triggers a kinesis which causes an increase in their random movement until they enter a more favourable environment, usually a darker moister area. Single cell algae are photosynthetic and have pigments that act as receptors which allow the alga to respond to directional stimuli such as light. On detection it causes a positive phototaxis which moves it towards the light for photosynthesis. Other autotrophic organisms such as plants are phototrophic and grow towards the directional light stimulus. Here again the pigment chlorophyll in the chloroplasts of palisade cells is acting as the light receptor.

For a larger and mobile organism to move and coordinate effectively in its environment it is at an advantage if it can detect light energy and see. In animals, the receptor surface is the retina of the eye which comprises the receptor cells, rods and cones. The cone cells are located primarily in the central region of the retina called the fovea. Each contains one of three kinds of the pigment iodopsin which will breakdown, or bleach, on absorption of a specific wavelength of light. This bleaching causes a chemical change which leads to changes in the permeability of the attached bipolar cell's membrane to sodium ions. This causes a depolarisation of the bipolar cell which initiates a nerve impulse in the optical nerve. Each cone has a single attachment to the optic nerve and so the cones at the fovea can send large amounts of information to the sensory areas of the cerebral hemispheres which can process the information and create vision of high acuity. The rods are more abundant at the periphery and many are connected to one bipolar cell. This arrangement causes a summation of signal and increases the chances of a generator potential being formed at lower light levels at the expense of visual acuity. In this way, information about the environment is detected and passed on to the brain to be processed to create a visual image of the world around us in a variety of lighting condition.

In moving through its environment the animal will be in contact with the ground and be touching and sensing constantly. On touching a tree for example, Pacinian receptors under the skin of a bear will detect the changes in pressure. The stretch-mediated sodium channels will open allowing sodium ions to enter and depolarise the axon generating a generator potential which send impulses along the axon of the attached sensory nerve. The information can them be processed by the brain. The animal may also encounter changes in temperature. In order to maintain the homeostasis of its internal environment it would have to respond by either increasing or decreasing metabolic rate and initiating mechanisms to lose or gain heat. Temperature receptors on the surface of the skin can detect warm or cold conditions. For example, on activation, cold receptors establish a generator potential and send impulses to the heat gain centre of the hypothalamus. As a result, this increases its frequency of impulses to effectors such as muscles in the arterioles close to the skins causing vasoconstriction and the contraction of erector muscles on the skin to cause the hair stand up and provide insulation.

Another response to low temperature is the onset of shivering, uncontrollable muscle contractions in the core that increases the rate of respiration and generates more heat internally. However this will release carbon dioxide as a waste product and increase the oxygen demand of the respiring tissues. To compensate, heart rate must increase to deliver more blood to the lungs for gas exchange. The carbon dioxide dissolves in the blood plasma and releases hydrogen ions which lower pH. This is detected by chemoreceptors in the aorta and carotid artery which send impulses on to the cardio-accelerator centre in the medulla oblongata of the brain. In turn this sends an increased frequency of impulses by a sympathetic pathway to the sino-atrial node of the heart to increase the rate at which it sends waves of excitation over the atria.

The heart can also respond to changes in blood pressure. If blood pressure is lower than normal, pressure (or baro) receptors in the aorta send impulses to the cardio-inhibitor centre which increases the frequency of parasympathetic impulses to the sino-atrial node reducing the frequency of contraction. Using these autonomic pathways, the body is able to maintain its constant internal environment.

Internal coordination may also be hormonal in nature and here the chemoreceptor plays a key role. Chemoreceptors are often protein molecules with a specific three dimensional shape that is complementary to a given chemical stimulus. It is this complementary nature that ensures that only one specific stimulus is responded to. When starch is taken in as food and digested by the enzymes amylase and maltase into glucose, the glucose is absorbed into the blood plasma by sodium-glucose co-transport. The increased glucose concentration causes the blood water potential to reduce which may prove harmful. The increase in glucose is therefore detected by a glucose receptor on the surface of the beta-cells of the islets of Langerhan in the pancreas. The receptor triggers a release of a protein hormone, insulin which in turn travels to the liver. Here it binds to another specific receptor on the cell surface membrane of hepatocytes forming a hormone-receptor complex. This alters the shape of the receptor triggering the activation of phosphorylase enzymes which condense glucose into glycogen in glycogenesis leading to the lowering of blood glucose.

Chemoreceptors are also important preventing disease. Phagocytes which circulate in blood have receptors on their surface that are complementary to the antigens on the surface of pathogens such as bacteria and viruses. On binding, the process of phagocytosis is initiated which leads to the engulfing of the pathogen and its subsequent destruction in the phagocytic vesicle by lysosomes. The presentation of this antigen on the surface of the cell allows the binding and recognition by B and T cells which can further coordinate a more specific response to the infection and contribute to health.

ESSAY 17: THE PATHWAYS OF SYNTHESIS OF CARBOHYDRATES FROM CARBON DIOXIDE

Carbohydrates are a range of compounds containing carbon, hydrogen and oxygen which play key roles in organisms. They are synthesised by autotrophs such as plants by the process of photosynthesis and then processed into other useful products. This essay will describe the how carbohydrates are synthesised from atmospheric carbon dioxide.

The carbon cycle is of major importance to life on Earth. One key source of carbon is atmospheric carbon dioxide. The plants act as producers by taking in this CO_2 and converting it into usable forms of energy for consumers. The gas exchange surface of the plant is on the underside of the leaf. Small pores, called stomata allow the diffusion of carbon dioxide into the air spaces as oxygen diffuses out. The thin structure of the leaf minimises the diffusion pathway and the round mesophyll cells offer an increased surface area for the process. The air spaces allow a rapid spreading and expansion of the CO_2 up through the leaf towards the palisade cells down a concentration gradient by diffusion. The cell surface membrane of the palisade cells is a hydrophobic lipid barrier which normally excludes hydrophilic molecules. Carbon dioxide is a non-polar molecule and is hydrophobic, and so can diffuse directly into the cytoplasm of the cell. From here it is transported to the chloroplast in readiness for its reduction to carbohydrate.

The palisade cells close to the upper surface of the leaf are adapted for photosynthesis in that they have a blocky shape that allows them to stack close together to offer a high surface area of the absorption of light energy. They contain many specialised organelles called chloroplasts which have an ultra-structure that is adapted to absorb light energy and synthesise carbohydrates. Within the stroma lie stacks of grana interconnected by thylakoid membranes which are the light of the light-dependent reaction. These membranes appear green under a light microscope due to the abundance of the pigment chlorophyll. The chlorophyll absorbs red and blue light and reflects the green. The energy is used to excite electrons on the chlorophyll to a higher energy level. This prompts the breakdown of water by photolysis, releasing oxygen gas as waste and hydrogen ions. The two electrons released are used to replace those excited. The excited electrons are then passed down a chain of carrier molecules in a series of redox reactions. As the electrons traverse the electron transport chain they release energy, and this is used to synthesise the immediate energy source, ATP from ADP and Pi by ATPase. This process of photo-phosphorylation generates the energy source that will be used later to form carbohydrates. Together with the hydrogen ions released by photolysis, the electrons eventually combine with a coenzyme NADP to form reduced NADP which then diffuses with the ATP out of the thylakoid into the surrounding stroma.

The carbon dioxide now enters the stroma and is combined immediately with a five-carbon sugar ribulose bisphosphate, RuBP. This conversion helps to maintain the diffusion gradient to bring in more CO_2. The six-carbon intermediate formed is unstable and breaks apart into two molecules of glycerate-3-phosphate. These are then reduced by the products of the light-dependent reaction, reduced NADP supplies the hydrogen ions and electrons while ATP supplies the energy. This produces the compound triose phosphate, a three carbon sugar molecule that is a derivative of class of carbohydrates called monosaccharides.

Five out of every six of these formed are used to regenerate the RuBP used earlier. The rest can now act a source for the synthesis of other important carbohydrates. Glucose is a six carbon monosaccharide that is formed from the combination of two triose molecules. The glucose is used widely as an energy source for respiration and requires transportation to other regions for this purpose. Glucose can undergo isomerism by isomerise enzymes forming other compounds with the formula $C_6H_{12}O_6$ such as fructose. Fructose and glucose can combine by condensation reaction to form the transport sugar sucrose. This disaccharide is linked by a strong glycosidic link and is transported by mass transport in the phloem to sink regions such as fruits, shoots and roots as an energy supply.

Glucose can also be condensed by enzymes to form more complex polysaccharides such as starch. Starch is a molecule comprising two separate polymers, amylose and amylopectin. *Amylose* is made from long unbranched chains of α-glucose that coil to give a compact shape for high density storage. In contrast *Amylopectin* is formed from long branched chains of α-glucose that allow enzymes to hydrolyse the glycosidic link to release glucose for energy more quickly. Both forms are insoluble making starch a useful storage substance that is not each washed away or affects water potential.

Another isomer of glucose is β-glucose. This differs from α-glucose only in the orientation of the H and OH groups of one of the carbon atoms. These can condense to form another useful polysaccharide, cellulose that is a key component of cell walls. This is composed of long unbranched chains of β-glucose that associate by hydrogen bonding to form strong microfibrils. These can weave together to give strength to the plant cell wall to prevent osmotic lysis.

ESSAY 18: PROTEINS SUCH AS INSULIN, SUCH AS INSULIN, FSH OR AN ANTI-INFLUENZA ANTIBODY ARE MADE IN CELLS THAT ARE REMOTE FROM THEIR TARGET TISSUES. DESCRIBE HOW ONE OF THESE IS SYNTHESISED AND EXERTS AN EFFECT ELSEWHERE.

Antibodies are proteins released from plasma cells (differentiated B cells) in response to specific antigens. Their role is to bind to, and precipitate these antigens and render the pathogen inactive. This essay will describe how these anti-influenza antibodies are synthesised and perform this role.

Influenza is a virus that infects humans. It enters the lungs via ventilation system and breaches the gas exchange surface (the lungs) and enters the epithelial cells. Here it enters the nucleus and uses endonuclease enzymes to seal its DNA across that of the host. This alters the control and regulation of the cells. On replication of the DNA, the DNA of the virus is also replicated and through differential gene expression, this alters the antigens that are expressed on the surface of the cells, altering their shape. The damaged cells may release locally-acting chemical mediators such as prostaglandins or histamine to increase the permeability of the capillaries to white cells such as T lymphocytes to coordinate the immune response.

T lymphocytes are a class of white blood cell involved in cell-mediated immunity that targets antigens that are non-host. An antigen is any structure that identifies a structure as non-host and the T cells have receptors that have a complementary shape that can bind and recognise them. Upon binding to the antigens on the surface of the infected cell a T-memory cell will become activated and divide by mitosis to form clones which differentiate into more memory cells (to provide a longer term immunity and a faster secondary response), a T-killer cell that binds and destroys the infected cells causing the lysis of its cell membrane, and a T-helper cell which releases cytokines that activate B-cells.

The B cells are another class of lymphocyte involved in humoral immunity. Once activated, they divide by mitosis and differentiate into B-memory and plasma cells. The plasma cells have the capacity to produce a specific antibody that is a protein which can be released to cause the precipitation of the invading pathogen.

The antibody they release is a y-shaped globular protein with a constant region and a variable region that has a complementary shape to the target antigen, in this case a part of the influenza-causing virus. The T-helper cell had released cytokines which bound to specific receptors of the cell surface membrane of the B cell. This activation triggered a differential gene expression which caused specialisation into an antibody-secreting B-cell. A part of this specialisation involved the expression of the gene for the antibody itself. In the plasma cell's nucleus the process of transcription resulted in the formation of an mRNA.

The enzyme helicase binds to the gene locus causing DNA to unwind and reveal a template strand. RNA-nucleotides bind by specific base pairing and RNA polymerase joins them by condensation to form a strand of pre-mRNA. Introns (non-coding regions) are then removed and the exons (coding regions) are spliced together with enzymes to form the mRNA which is small enough to diffuse through the nuclear pore and bind to a ribosome on the rough endoplasmic reticulum. The process of protein synthesis or translation can now begin. In the cytoplasm, a transfer RNA (tRNA) molecule binds to a specific amino acid and two such complexes deliver their amino acids to the ribosome. The anticodon on tRNA binds to the complementary codon on mRNA by specific base pairing (A to U, C to G). An enzyme now forms the peptide bond between the amino acids by condensation using energy from ATP and the process is repeated building up the polypeptide chain.

The protein is now packaged into vesicles from the rough endoplasmic reticulum and transported to the Golgi apparatus where it is folded and adopts the y-shaped specific three dimensional structure of the antibody. Here it is packaged into vesicles in readiness for secretion. The vesicles are pushed towards the B-cell's membrane using energy supplied by ATP in the same way as synaptic vesicles containing acetylcholine are pushed to a presynaptic membrane. The vesicles fuse and release their contents into the blood plasma by exocytosis.

The antibody then travels around the blood dissolved in the blood plasma. The pressure to push it through the blood vessels comes from contraction of the ventricles in the heart which creates a high hydrostatic pressure which forces blood into tissues through the arteries, arterioles and capillaries. When the antibody comes into contact with the influenza virus, the complementary shape of the variable region allows it to form a specific attachment to the antigens on the pathogen's surface. The hinge region of the antibody allows it to swivel and bind to a second pathogen. In this way and antigen-antibody complex is formed which eventually leads to the precipitation, or agglutination of the pathogen particles. Phagocyte cells are then attracted in and will engulf the agglutinated complex into a phagocytic vacuole where its lysosomes will release enzymes to destroy the pathogen.

ESSAY 19: PERFORM A CRITICAL ANALYSIS OF THE METHODS USED TO COLLECT BIOLOGICAL DATA

Studies of biological processes, mechanisms and events involve the collection of data that must be reliable, precise and above all accurate. Such data provide the evidence and quantitative values on which statistical tests can be performed to draw conclusions about the world around us. This essay will describe some of the methods used to collect data with an emphasis on criticising their usefulness.

The study of biology spans many levels from the molecular and cellular to the tissues, organs and systems that make up individual organisms to their association in populations and their interactions in communities and ecosystems. Accordingly study of these different levels requires different experimental and data collection strategies. However in general there are certain in-built requirements for a study to be valid.

The data collected should be recorded *objectively* rather than *subjectively*. Each individual views the world differently and a reliance on a subjective measurement by an individual does not provide a rigorous basis on which to draw conclusions. The data should be quantitative rather than qualitative. It may be possible to qualitatively state that one population of organisms is taller than another, but quantitative data enumerates the study and allows manipulation of the data and for us to decide *by how much* they differ. For example, in comparing the heights of male A2 chemistry students to biology students would involve recording the heights of each student using suitable measuring device and then averaging them. The standard deviation would provide evidence of spread about the mean which would then allow comparisons by conversion to a standard error and 95% confidence intervals. This and other types of data collections then allow statistical testing to assign a certain degree of significance to the data and an indication that any differences in the results were due to chance.

Statistical testing is the cornerstone of research studies as it provides a clear and objective indication as to the significance of the information collected. But the usefulness of statistical tests is hampered by the sample sizes chosen in the study and the means by which the data was collected. It is not possible to collect data on all the organisms in an ecosystem for example, so samples must be used that are random in order to eliminate any bias. Repeats are taken to further increase the reliability of the data collected. If too few samples are taken then the statistical significance of the results is impaired. For example it may happen by chance that five students chosen are taller than the average and so a comparison to a small group of other students may prove invalid. On the flipside of the coin is the realisation that too many samples require more time and organisation and creates greater difficulties in the organisation and handling of the data. So it is important that the study is designed carefully to get a balance between the practical aspects of the study and the statistical relevance of the sample sizes chosen.

Quantifying habitats and ecological systems pose unique difficulties. Habitats are dynamic in that organisms are constantly growing and changing within their environment. Many animals will migrate into or emigrate out of a region under study which complicates the analysis, necessitating the need for mark-release-capture techniques which are prone to significant errors caused by the high sampling size needed to get any degree of accuracy. Seasonal changes will render conclusions drawn in winter for example, less reliable in summer when other organisms proliferate and the competitions and interactions between the plants and animals are completely different. Care must therefore be taken in drawing conclusions about specific habits and studies can only be compared if they are matched for the time of year that the data were collected.

The abundance and distribution of small plants can be studied using quadrats and transects. Problems that have previously been discussed are relevant here also as the distribution of organisms is rarely even and so unless large number of repeat samples is taken over the area studied, the data may not be reliable. These large numbers are however time consuming to perform. Also, bias may play a large role in the choice of which area to study and so it is imperative to divide an area of study up into a grid and use a random number generator to assign coordinates to the particular areas the quadrats are placed. Quadrats are however intrinsically limited in the size of the organisms they can contain. Studies of woodland habitats to making assessments of stages of succession for example would be hampered by quadrats as the shrubs and trees would not fit inside it. Measurements of dry biomass are equally limited as larger shrubs and trees would not fit into a suitable oven for drying!

Also in the laboratory the methods of data collection have limitations which may affect their usefulness and the ability to draw conclusions in a study. For example, when measurements of gas volumes are taken using a gas syringe to study the rates of enzyme controlled reactions, they rely on timed points and it requires at least two individuals to take accurate measurement, one to read the clock time and the other to note the gas volume. But because the gas volume change is dynamic, a delayed reaction time of the operator can introduce inaccuracies.

The equipment itself has an inbuilt imprecision. For example using a thermometer that only detects $1°C$ temperature changes yields less precise data that one that measures to $0.1°C$. A gas syringe may only detect gas volumes within a precision of $1cm^3$ which may further limit the ability to quantify rates of reaction at lower temperatures of enzyme concentrations.

Some studies may involve the magnification of cell or tissue samples. In some cases simply counting non-motile cells can be achieved with a haemocytometer under a microscope by motile cells such as sperm are constantly moving which decreases the accuracy of the counts.

While light microscopes can be used to view single cells at reasonable magnification they do not generate a high enough resolution to view detail inside of cells. Some studies may also require the use of electron microscopes to view intracellular details at high resolution. While these can generate very high resolution images for analysis of tissues and cells, they are very expensive, and require the sample to be non-living as the electron beam passes through a vacuum. Because they can only be used on very thin samples they are prone to generating artifacts in the results which may impair interpretation.

ESSAY 20: THE PHYSIOLOGICAL AND ECOLOGICAL EFFECTS ON ORGANISMS OF AN INCREASE IN GLOBAL TEMPERATURES

A rise in the environmental temperature can affect many types of organisms either in adverse and beneficial ways. The effects can lead to changes in the metabolic processes inside the organisms and over time can force adaptation and natural selection which may shape the interactions of the organisms within their niche. This essay will specify some of those effects and describe their ecological impact.

Microorganisms such as bacteria and fungi do not have complex homeostatic mechanisms to control their body temperatures. An increase in the environmental temperature will therefore have a profound effect on their metabolism. Enzyme activities will increase due to the increased kinetic energy given to the enzyme and substrate molecules which will increase their rates of respiration. In turn they are able to replicate more quickly as more ATP is made available for growth. Microbes occupy a variety of niches including acting as decomposers. An increase in respiration rates and numbers of saprobiotic organisms will increase decomposition rates and carbon and nitrogen recycling. Their carbon recycling releases more carbon dioxide as the waste product of aerobic respiration which would further add to global warming as it is a greenhouse gas. As many microbes are pathogenic the increased growth rates will also increase the mutation rate possibly leading to the production of more pathogenic forms. The antigenic variability that results from the changes in the gene sequence will allow some of these forms to evade the host immune systems of the animals they infect, increasing the incidence of disease.

Many single-celled photosynthetic algae will also have their growth rates increased in the same way. The increased nitrate recycling caused by the growth of nitrifying bacteria will allow greater leaching of nitrate into water courses. This nitrate is a limiting factor for the growth of the algae across the surface of the water. The algae would bloom covering the surface and out-compete the submerged aquatic plants causing their death. This will in turn lead to a rapid growth in numbers of decomposer bacteria which aerobically respire and increase the biological oxygen demand. The reduction in oxygen levels will cause the death of fish and other aquatic life and allow the proliferation of other anaerobic organisms. This eutrophication process will dramatically reduce the diversity index and completely destabilise any food webs associated with this ecosystem.

Plants are the main producers for the food webs in an ecosystem. They are autotrophic and photosynthesise to produce energy in form of carbohydrates. The passage of water through the plant is called transpiration and this process will be accelerated at higher temperatures. Plants obtain ions and water from the soil by active transport of mineral ions. This lowers water potential inside the root hair cells which then causes the absorption of water by osmosis. The water then passes through the cortex by the apoplast and symplast pathways and enters the xylem where it ultimately causes a root pressure which pushes water up the xylem. Evaporation of water from the mesophyll cells and its loss through the stomata creates a water potential gradient (a tension) that draws water from the xylem to replace that which was lost. The water molecules have hydrogen bonds between adjacent molecules cohesion) which draws the water up the xylem in a column. Higher temperatures would mean a faster rate of transpiration and so over time would force xerophytic adaptations through natural selection such as a selection for reduced surface area to volume ratio like cacti, rolled leaves and sunken stomata. Such changes are likely to reduce biodiversity of plants as fewer species are adapted for hotter and drier climates. In turn, this would reduce productivity and the range of plants in a given area, meaning fewer habitats and food sources for animals, birds and insects etc.

The drop in productivity and diversity index would therefore lead to a destabilisation of food webs which would lead to dramatic reductions in population numbers, creating genetic bottlenecks. These bottlenecks result when a large reduction in a population reduces the range of alleles in the gene pools. The surviving population is less able to adapt to the new conditions and so increases the chances of extinction, a fate that would further contribute to the destabilisation of the remaining food webs.

Endothermic mammals too would experience physiological effects of temperature rises. Thermo-receptors on the skin would be activated more and send a greater frequency of impulses along sensory nerves to the heat loss centre. This centre, in the hypothalamus of the brain, would be active for a greater amount of time to send impulses to effectors which increase the rate of sweating, vasodilation and decrease metabolic rate. Such longer term physiological changes would therefore impose selection pressures that would select for less body hair and a leaner body with a higher surface area to volume ratio to dissipate heat more effectively. One other physiological effect may be to alter the position of the oxygen dissociation curve of haemoglobin. A shift to the left would mean that less oxygen becomes unloaded due to an increased affinity since the rate of respiration is reduced.

Ecothermic reptiles such as lizards would be active for more of the daytime and their behavioural adaptations such as basking would help maintain their metabolism at optimum conditions. These organisms derive their energy mainly from the surroundings, and a warmer climate would increase their chances of competing with endotherms. Once again, this shift in the ecological balance could have profound consequences for the food webs and affect the species diversity and the chances of survival of many struggling populations of organisms.

COMING SOON

from

CT Publications

May 2010

✓ AQA A2 Biology: Writing the Synoptic Essay e-book
✓ AQA AS CHEM5 Cheat sheets
✓ AQA A2 BIOL5 Cheat sheets

July 2010

✓ Surviving maths in AS Chemistry
✓ Surviving maths in AS Biology

August 2010

✓ AQA AS Chemistry: How Science Works
✓ AQA AS Biology: How Science Works

September 2010

✓ The ultimate AQA AS Chemistry Unit 1 exam preparation guide
✓ The ultimate AQA AS Biology Unit 1 exam preparation guide

All books are also available as e-books and can be downloaded instantly at
www.ctpublications.co.uk

or

ordered by e-mail at orders@chemistrytextbooks.co.uk